About APS PRESS

APS PRESS, the nonprofit publishing imprint of The American Phytopathological Society, has published more than 300 titles, including the Compendium of Plant Disease Series, the Plant Health Management Series, and the Farmer's Guide to Crop Diseases Series. APS PRESS books and digital products are used by educators, students, plant scientists, Extension specialists, crop consultants, county agents, growers, master gardeners, horticulture specialists, nursery and landscape workers, greenhouse employees, forestry specialists, plant pathologists, mycologists, nematologists, virologists, entomologists, weed scientists, and plant molecular biologists, among others. APS PRESS is guided by a volunteer editorial board composed of scientists from all major areas of plant pathology.

D0989146

A FARMER'S GUIDE TO
Corn Diseases

EDITED BY

Kiersten Wise

Purdue University
West Lafayette, Indiana, U.S.A.

Daren Mueller

Iowa State University
Ames, Iowa, U.S.A.

Adam Sisson

Iowa State University
Ames, Iowa, U.S.A.

Damon Smith

University of Wisconsin–Madison
Madison, Wisconsin, U.S.A.

Carl Bradley

University of Kentucky
Princeton, Kentucky, U.S.A.

Alison Robertson

Iowa State University
Ames, Iowa, U.S.A.

The American Phytopathological Society
St. Paul, Minnesota, U.S.A.

The information in this book is a general guide for disease diagnosis and management. It represents the knowledge of authors, reviewers, and editors at the time of publication and is not intended to be exhaustive. Disease information and management recommendations may vary by region and specific farm conditions. Users should consult local Extension agents or crop management specialists for area-specific recommendations.

Reference in this publication to any specific commercial product, process, or service or the use of any trade, firm, or corporation name is for general informational purposes only and does not constitute an endorsement, recommendation, or certification of any kind by the authors, editors, reviewers, publisher, or others involved with this publication. Individuals using such products assume responsibility for their use in accordance with the current directions provided by the manufacturer. The authors, editors, reviewers, publisher, and others involved with this publication make no warranty regarding the use of this information and will not be held liable for any damages resulting from subsequent decisions made by end users.

The disease distribution maps found in this book are general diagnostic tools and represent the knowledge of the authors, reviewers, editors, and other subject matter authorities at the time of publication. Diseases may be present in areas not specified on the maps for a number of reasons, including expansion of the disease range because of movement of pathogens, changing weather patterns, and pathogen genetics; lack of complete distribution information at the initial date of publication; and new discoveries made postpublication. The authors, editors, reviewers, publisher, and others involved with this publication make no warranty regarding the use of disease distribution data presented or not presented here and will not be held liable for any damages resulting from subsequent decisions made by end users.

Library of Congress Control Number: 2016932301
International Standard Book Numbers:
Print: 978-0-89054-454-9
eBook: 978-0-89054-511-9
Online: 978-0-89054-512-6

Printed in the United States of America on acid-free paper.

The American Phytopathological Society
3340 Pilot Knob Road
St. Paul, Minnesota 55121, U.S.A.

Corn (*Zea mays* L.) has evolved into a major grain crop that is essential for food and fuel in the United States and Canada. The United States is the world's number-one producer of corn, growing tens of billions of bushels annually. Record corn yields have made corn a profitable and important field crop in North America.

When a crop has high value and demand, protecting its yield potential is essential to reaping the greatest economic returns. Doing so means keeping the crop as healthy as possible—a goal that involves disease management. The cornerstone of effective disease management is accurate disease diagnosis. However, as farmers become more aware of how diseases affect corn yields, they may be overwhelmed by the number of diseases that can be present on corn and struggle to diagnose and manage diseases of importance.

The purpose of *A Farmer's Guide to Corn Diseases* is to provide an overview of the corn diseases that occur in the United States and Canada, with an emphasis on diagnosing diseases in the field setting. This guide explains the factors that make plants unhealthy, including plant pathogens. It also presents brief summaries of prevalent corn diseases. Each disease summary includes sections that describe symptoms and signs of the disease, identify diseases and disorders with similar symptoms and signs, state the conditions that favor disease development, and review basic management options.

The information presented for each disease is based on *Compendium of Corn Diseases, Fourth Edition,* edited by Gary P. Munkvold and Donald G. White (American Phytopathological Society, 2016). However, additional information is also provided to aid in diagnosis—for instance, key diagnostic terms and disease distribution maps. *A Farmer's Guide to Corn Diseases* is not intended to provide an exhaustive discussion of every disease that occurs on corn, and management recommendations are intentionally generalized to encourage readers to contact state and provincial Extension personnel or crop management specialists for region-specific management options.

Although this guide focuses on corn diseases that occur in the United States and Canada, many other diseases have global importance. Some of these diseases are addressed in Chapter 9. Farmers should be aware of disease issues that may be of future importance to the United States and Canada.

Producing *A Farmer's Guide to Corn Diseases* truly has been a collaborative effort. Fifty-nine contributors from more than 25 universities, agencies, and companies were consulted for their expertise with particular diseases. These contributors dedicated their time to editing sections, supplying images, and providing input on the development and direction of this book. The result is the first comprehensive overview of corn diseases across the United States and Canada written with an audience of farmers in mind.

As corn production practices advance and as environments change, so will the disease issues of importance. This guide is meant to be an evolving reference, and making updates and additions will be critical to maintaining its relevance. We encourage readers to offer feedback and suggestions to help improve this book, as we aim to improve the quality of disease references available to individuals involved in corn production.

Acknowledgments

The editors thank the many authors, editors, and contributors to this publication, especially Doug Jardine, Jerald Pataky, Albert Tenuta, and Paul Vincelli for their thorough review of the materials. Authors are listed in the Contributors section that follows, and individuals who contributed drawings and photographs are listed in the Image Credits section at the end of the book.

Special thanks to the U.S. Department of Agriculture National Institute of Food and Agriculture (USDA–NIFA) for supporting integrated pest management (IPM).

Kiersten Wise
Daren Mueller
Adam Sisson
Damon Smith
Carl Bradley
Alison Robertson

CONTRIBUTORS

Reviewers

Doug Jardine, Kansas State University

Jerald Pataky, University of Illinois (retired)

Albert Tenuta, Ontario Ministry of Agriculture, Food and Rural Affairs (OMAFRA)

Paul Vincelli, University of Kentucky

Authors

Tom Allen, Mississippi State University
Sections 4.20, Sorghum Downy Mildew;
4.21, Southern Corn Leaf Blight

Gary C. Bergstrom, Cornell University
Sections 6.6, Gibberella Crown and Stalk Rot;
7.1, Mycotoxins; 7.6, Gibberella Ear Rot
and Mycotoxins

Carl Bradley, University of Kentucky
Sections 4.7, Diplodia Leaf Streak; 4.17, Northern
Corn Leaf Blight

Emmanuel Byamukama, South Dakota State
University
Section 6.7, Pythium Stalk Rot

Jim Camberato, Purdue University
Section 8.1, Nutrient and Fertilizer Disorders

Martin Chilvers, Michigan State University
Sections 5.2, Pythium Seedling Blight and Root Rot;
5.4, Rhizoctonia Crown and Brace Root Rot

William Dolezal, Pioneer Hi-Bred International, Inc.
Section 4.2, Banded Leaf and Sheath Blight;
Chapter 9, Diseases of Worldwide Importance

Paul Esker, Universidad de Costa Rica
Sections 4.1, Anthracnose Leaf Blight;
6.1, Anthracnose Stalk Rot

Travis Faske, University of Arkansas
Section 6.2, Bacterial Stalk Rot

Andrew Friskop, North Dakota State University
Section 4.4, Common Smut

Clayton Hollier, Louisiana State University
Section 4.22, Southern Rust

Tom Isakeit, Texas A&M University
Section 7.2, Aspergillus Ear Rot
and Aflatoxin

Tamra Jackson-Ziems, University of
Nebraska–Lincoln
Sections 5.5, Root-Lesion Nematode;
5.6, Sting and Needle Nematodes;
5.7, Other Nematodes

Doug Jardine, Kansas State University
Sections 4.11, Head Smut;
4.12, Holcus Leaf Spot

Laura Jesse, Iowa State University
Chapter 10, A Closer Look

Heather M. Kelly, University of Tennessee
Sections 6.3, Charcoal Rot; 6.5, Fusarium
Stalk Rot

Nathan Kleczewski, University of Delaware
Section 4.3, Common Rust

Travis Legleiter, Purdue University
Section 8.2, Chemical Injury

Mark Licht, Iowa State University
Chapter 2, Understanding Corn Diseases
and Disorders (The Corn Plant);
Section 8.3, Environmental Conditions
and Genetic Disorders

Dean Malvick, University of Minnesota
Sections 4.8, Eyespot; 5.3, Red Root Rot

Daren Mueller, Iowa State University
Chapter 1, How to Use This Book;
Chapter 2, Understanding Corn Diseases
and Disorders (Impact of Diseases on Corn,
Infectious Diseases, Noninfectious Disorders);
Chapter 3, Diagnostic Key

Gary Munkvold, Iowa State University
Section 7.5, Fusarium Ear Rot and Fumonisin

John Obermeyer, Purdue University
Section 8.4, Insect Injury

Jerald Pataky, University of Illinois (retired)
Sections 4.5, Corn Stunt; 4.13, Maize Bushy Stunt;
4.14, Maize Chlorotic Dwarf; 4.15, Maize
Chlorotic Mottle; 4.16, Maize Dwarf Mosaic;
Chapter 9, Diseases of Worldwide Importance

Pierce Anderson Paul, The Ohio State University
Section 4.10, Gray Leaf Spot

Trey Price, Louisiana State University
Section 4.19, Physoderma Brown Spot and Stalk Rot

Alison Robertson, Iowa State University
Sections 4.9, Goss's Wilt; 5.1, Fusarium Crown
and Root Rot

Adam Sisson, Iowa State University
Chapter 1, How to Use This Book;
Chapter 2, Understanding Corn Diseases
and Disorders (Impact of Diseases on Corn,
Infectious Diseases, Noninfectious Disorders);
Chapter 3, Diagnostic Key

Damon Smith, University of Wisconsin–Madison
Section 4.24, Other Viruses

Laura Sweets, University of Missouri
Sections 4.18, Northern Corn Leaf Spot;
6.4, Diplodia Stalk Rot; 7.4, Diplodia Ear Rot

Albert Tenuta, Ontario Ministry of Agriculture,
Food and Rural Affairs (OMAFRA)
Section 4.23, Stewart's Disease

Kiersten Wise, Purdue University
Preface; Section 4.6, Crazy Top of Corn;
7.1, Mycotoxins

Charles Woloshuk, Purdue University
Sections 7.3, Cladosporium Ear Rot; 7.7, Nigrospora
Ear Rot; 7.8, Penicillium Ear Rot; 7.9, Trichoderma
Ear Rot

CONTENTS

A FARMER'S GUIDE TO
Corn Diseases

Introduction

CHAPTER 1

How to Use This Book

Plant disease diagnosis becomes easier with experience. Trained agronomists and plant pathologists automatically think about the factors that influence disease development when they walk into a field. Those factors include crop growth stage, recent weather, field topography, time of year, symptom expression for particular diseases/disorders, and so on.

Having experience allows us to use these factors to narrow down the possible causes of a plant problem. When we have enough experience, these factors become ingrained in us, to the point that we think about them automatically. However, even individuals who are new to diagnosing plant disease can use and assimilate this information to help them determine which diseases or disorders may be affecting their crops.

It may seem like a lot of information is needed to simply identify a plant disease, but we are accustomed to processing large amounts of information automatically every day. Take driving, for example: We all start with the basics and have to practice processing information to be safe drivers. As we drive, we read the facial expressions of the drivers around us, identify an aggressive driver one stoplight ahead, assess the speed of traffic, and so on. Getting from point A to point B safely in a vehicle depends on performing the many small actions that comprise driving, but experienced drivers automatically think about these things while on the road.

Most of us were not good drivers initially, and those of us who have taught our children to drive may have experienced the frustration of helping them learn to process all the information necessary to drive safely. Good driving skills come with experience, just as accurate plant disease diagnosis comes with experience. Experience helps drivers filter out the many distractions, or "noise," on the street. Similarly, experience helps farmers and agronomists eliminate the "noise" in the field and focus instead on the probable cause of a prevailing issue in a particular field.

In this book, we use our experience and the expertise of others to help you understand the process of diagnosing plant disease. We have asked many experienced agronomists and plant pathologists about their thought processes when diagnosing field problems. Together, their answers provide a snapshot of how to eliminate the noise and focus on the problem. The information in Chapter 3, Diagnostic Key, will assist you in narrowing down the likely causes of field problems.

Once you have narrowed down the options, you can help confirm or further focus your diagnosis using the information and images in Chapters 4 through 9, which address specific diseases and disorders. As you gain experience, you will work through this process more quickly and gain confidence in your diagnostic skills.

CHAPTER 2

Understanding Corn Diseases and Disorders

Corn diseases reduce crop yields and grain and seed quality every year. Some diseases are common and result in negligible or consistent but relatively small losses, while others occur less frequently but sometimes cause severe damage to crops. The type, level, and magnitude of disease will change yearly and regionally and be significantly influenced by weather conditions.

Corn disease management begins with proper disease identification. This guide is intended to be a practical resource to aid farmers, Extension educators, and agribusiness professionals in identifying corn diseases. It also outlines general management options for specific diseases; however, certain situations may require different management strategies than those outlined here. It is essential to determine the economic feasibility of any course of action and to consider how it fits with the existing goals of the farm operation. Extension personnel in each state and province can assist farmers with developing situation-specific disease management plans to help reach the goal of producing a healthy crop (Fig. 2.1).

FIG. 2.1. Healthy cornfield.

IMPACT OF DISEASES ON CORN

Each year, corn diseases reduce yields in the United States and Canada. Annual U.S. losses are estimated to range from 2 to 15%. Disease impact varies from year to year depending on weather conditions, crop production practices, hybrid selection, susceptibility to disease, and geography, among other factors.

Which diseases are prevalent and economically important changes over time. For example, three corn diseases that were among the most prevalent in the U.S. Corn Belt in the 2010s—anthracnose stalk rot, gray leaf spot, and Goss's wilt—were of little or no importance in the United States and Canada before 1970. Pathogens continually evolve, and as they change, the risk and importance of certain diseases may change, as well. Hybrid genetics also change as breeders select for various characteristics, which may inadvertently impact a crop's susceptibility to disease. Similarly, changes in weather patterns and management practices affect disease development. Some diseases that caused great concern in the twentieth century are no longer major issues in corn production. For example, in the 1930s, Stewart's disease (caused by *Pantoea stewartii*—see Chapter 4, section 4.23) caused substantial losses in the United States and Canada, and as recently as the late 1990s, Stewart's wilt was a major concern in corn seed production in the United States (Fig. 2.2). However, today, the disease is found only sporadically in North America.

In many areas of the United States and Canada, the incidence of corn disease has either increased during the 2010s or is expected to increase because of several factors. Two key factors are the adoption of production practices that increase residue on the soil surface (such as reduced tillage and no-till) and the continuous production of corn without rotation to another crop. Also, high-yielding hybrids, which are widely grown, are sometimes developed from germplasm that has inadequate levels of resistance for all the conditions in which they are grown. In such cases, diseases may develop to levels that affect yields. Depending on the popularity of the hybrids and the germplasm from which they were developed, a season or two may pass before high-producing hybrids with adequate levels of resistance are once again available in the marketplace. Factors beyond farmers' control—such as overall increases in humidity and the frequency of heavy rainfall events—can also increase the likelihood that pathogens will cause disease.

A corn disease epidemic caused by a single pathogen can have wide-ranging and extremely damaging results. A classic example of this happened

FIG. 2.2. Light-green to yellow streaks on leaves are symptoms of Stewart's wilt.

FIG. 2.3. Hybrids susceptible to race T of the fungus that causes southern corn leaf blight (left) can be severely damaged by this disease.

in 1970, when race T of the southern corn leaf blight fungus (*Bipolaris maydis*—see Chapter 4, section 4.21) caused approximately $1 billion in corn crop losses (Fig. 2.3). Much of the corn planted in the United States and Canada was susceptible to this fungus, the weather was conducive to disease development, and the fungus spread via wind currents from the southern United States into the Corn Belt and then into Canada, causing devastating crop losses.

Losses from disease are not always directly tied to plant injury or disease symptoms. For example, economic losses can occur if a quarantined pathogen is detected in seed designated for export and that lot of corn is refused. Another example involves lodged corn, which takes extra time to harvest and can therefore affect profitability through lost time and higher fuel costs. In addition, grain buyers can discount corn when poor grain quality results from disease or when mycotoxins are produced in corn.

Grain prices also influence the potential for economic losses. A loss of 2 bushels per acre when corn is worth $2 per bushel has less economic impact than the same 2-bushel loss when corn is worth $5 per bushel. Disease losses occurring in sweet corn, seed corn, and popcorn may also be more economically important than disease losses in field corn because of the potentially higher value of these crops.

INFECTIOUS DISEASES

What Is Plant Disease?

The term plant disease can be defined as an abnormal change in the physical form or function of a plant over a period of time. Plant disease can reduce both yield and seed quality. Disease-causing agents include bacteria, fungi, oomycetes, viruses, and nematodes. Living organisms, such as bacteria and fungi, cause diseases, while nonliving agents, such as drought and nutrient deficiencies, cause disorders. Plant disorders are sometimes confused with infectious diseases, so it is critical to distinguish between diseases and disorders.

Changes in plant tissue color, shape, and function in response to disease are called symptoms. Visible effects of these changes include leaf spots and streaks, yellowing of leaves, plant stunting and wilting, and many others (Fig. 2.4). Plant pathogens cause symptoms in several ways. They may release toxins within the plant, break down and feed on plant tissue, restrict the plant's ability to obtain or transport water and nutrients, and cause other issues in the host. Each pathogen has evolved a unique niche or mode of causing infection, so that no two corn diseases are exactly alike.

Some pathogens produce unique or characteristic symptoms of disease that aid in identification. Other pathogens produce symptoms that are subtle and difficult to distinguish from those of other diseases and disorders, which may be similar. Moreover, symptoms on plants can change as the season progresses and be influenced by crop genetics, environmental conditions, and even host response to the pathogen. Some symptoms are found on only one type of plant tissue, such as the roots or stalks, while others are observed throughout the plant. Identifying a disease with nondescript symptoms often requires performing additional steps, including examining plants in the laboratory and looking for pathogen growth on plant tissue.

Physical components of plant pathogens are called signs. Fungal fruiting bodies (such as pycnidia,

FIG. 2.4. Blocky, tan spots are symptoms of gray leaf spot.

FIG. 2.5. Spores of the fungus that causes common rust on corn are a sign of the pathogen.

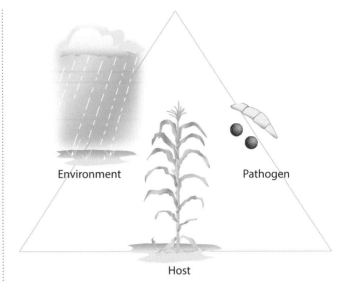

FIG. 2.6. Plant disease triangle. The three sides of the disease triangle are (1) a susceptible host, (2) a disease-causing pathogen, and (3) an environment suitable for disease development. If any of these elements is missing, plant disease will not occur.

spores, mycelium, and microsclerotia) and bacterial ooze from plant tissue are both examples of signs of plant pathogens (Fig. 2.5).

The Plant Disease Triangle

Plant disease can occur only if these three elements exist simultaneously (Fig. 2.6):

1. a susceptible host
2. a disease-causing pathogen
3. an environment suitable for disease development

A susceptible host is a plant that has been infected by and is providing a food source for a disease-causing pathogen. When a corn plant is the host to an invading organism, its own ability to develop or reproduce can be diminished.

Pathogens are disease-causing agents (Fig. 2.7). They are capable of entering a plant in a variety of ways, such as through wounds and natural openings. Some pathogens, including viruses, can be transmitted by insects that feed on plants.

Disease will not develop without a favorable environment, and the environmental conditions that favor different types of pathogens vary. Even highly susceptible corn hybrids exposed to pathogens will not exhibit symptoms when temperature and moisture levels are not conducive to disease development. This fact helps to explain why certain diseases are problematic one year but not another or in one specific location but not across an entire region.

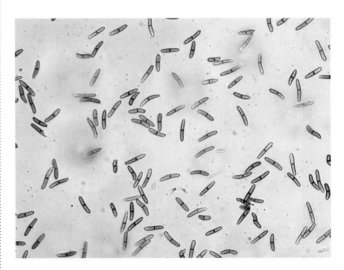

FIG. 2.7. Spores of the fungus that causes Diplodia leaf streak.

Almost all pathogens are sensitive to temperature and moisture levels in the air and soil (Fig. 2.8). These two attributes determine when many pathogens are physically able to infect plants, move through soil or on leaves, or produce reproductive structures in plant tissue. Each pathogen has a specific temperature or moisture range at which it is most active, and these ranges vary widely across pathogens.

FIG. 2.8. Moisture in the form of fog.

Plants' susceptibility to disease can also be influenced by temperature and moisture. For example, when growth or germination slows because of cool soil, young plants are more vulnerable to seedling diseases. Lack of moisture can also stress plants, making them more susceptible to disease. Other environmental factors that play a role in disease development are soil pH, soil texture and compaction, relative humidity levels, available nutrients, and light levels.

Temperature and moisture can also influence vectors of certain pathogens, such as plant viruses. Vectors include certain insects, plant-parasitic nematodes, and parasitic plants. Hot, dry conditions can increase the presence of some important insect vectors, while wet conditions might favor the presence of parasitic plants such as dodder. Understanding how weather affects vectors can facilitate making accurate plant disease diagnoses.

The use of management tools can remove or diminish elements of the disease triangle to prevent disease from occurring or to reduce its significance if it does occur. For instance, planting disease-resistant varieties reduces the impact of disease on the host, and destroying crop residue, rotating crops, applying pesticides, and managing insects that spread disease are means of diminishing the pathogen. Draining low areas of a field and changing row spacing are examples of eliminating environmental conditions that enhance disease development. Cultural practices such as tillage, residue management, seedbed preparation, planting date, and planting depth can affect disease development, as well.

Once again, plant disease can occur only if all three elements of the plant disease triangle are present. A plant disease epidemic can happen when all three elements occur simultaneously and at optimal levels.

Major Groups of Plant Pathogens
Fungi

Fungi are common plant pathogens that cause a variety of diseases, from root rots to foliar diseases. Not all fungi cause crop disease; many are actually beneficial. Fungi decompose organic matter (dead plants and animals) and can be harnessed to produce medicine and food.

The fungi that attack plants are typically very small and cannot be seen in detail without a microscope. However, extensive fungal growth, such as occurs with ear molds, can be seen on plant tissue.

Fungi obtain energy from dead or decaying plant and animal tissue or from a living host. Fungi cannot produce food the way plants do, because they lack chlorophyll (the compound that allows plants to carry out photosynthesis).

The majority of fungal organisms are made of hyphae (singular: hypha): threadlike strands of fungal mycelium that extract nutrients and water from a host. Hyphae can also produce toxins, enzymes, and other chemicals. These substances influence disease progression and symptom expression in an infected host.

A mass or network of hyphae is called mycelium (plural: mycelia). Mycelium is often not visible, because it develops inside host tissue. Sometimes, mycelium can be seen on host surface tissue. An example is the fuzzy, white growth of the fungus that causes Diplodia ear rot (Fig. 2.9).

The most common way for fungi to reproduce and spread is through spores, which have the ability to initiate new infections (Fig. 2.10). Water and wind are the primary methods for moving spores from plant to plant and to new geographic areas. Spores of fungi that cause diseases such as common rust and southern rust can travel long distances on wind currents. Some fungi produce specialized structures known as fruiting bodies, which contain spores. Fungi may survive long periods in soil or on dead plant tissue as specialized, toughened spores or fruiting bodies. Identification of fungi is sometimes accomplished by looking at spores and fruiting bodies under magnification.

Symptoms of fungal diseases vary and include leaf lesions or discoloration, decaying roots, seedling blight, plant wilting, and discolored seeds. Signs of fungal diseases include mycelium on the leaf surface, fruiting bodies (such as pycnidia) on stems, and fuzzy mycelial growth.

Oomycetes

Oomycetes resemble fungi in appearance, and like fungi, they are composed of mycelia. However, oomycetes have several characteristics that differentiate them from fungi. The cell walls of oomycetes are composed of cellulose, whereas the cell walls of fungi are composed of chitin. Oomycetes produce spores that have tail-like structures called flagella, which enable them to swim in water (Fig. 2.11). Consequently, saturated soil conditions favor spore production and infection of plants.

The plant diseases caused by oomycetes are among the most devastating and economically important and have played an important role in history. For

FIG. 2.9. Mycelium of the fungus that causes Diplodia ear rot.

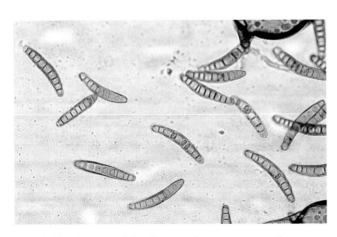

FIG. 2.10. Spores of the fungus that causes northern corn leaf spot.

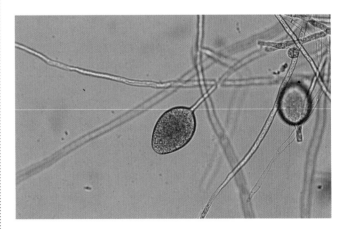

FIG. 2.11. Oomycete oospores and zoospores.

example, the Irish potato famine of the mid-1800s was caused by the disease late blight, for which the pathogen is the oomycete *Phytophthora infestans*.

Symptoms of oomycete diseases include leaf lesions and discoloration, stem lesions, root decay, seedling blight, plant wilting, and seed discoloration.

Bacteria

Bacteria also cause some of the most important corn diseases, such as Goss's wilt. Bacteria reproduce by splitting in half and can increase very quickly in population. Under ideal conditions, a single bacterium splitting once every half hour will grow to more than 250 trillion bacteria in a day's time.

Colonies of bacteria form when many bacterial cells clump together (Fig. 2.12). Colony characteristics—such as color, shape, and size— can help to identify bacteria. Very large clumps of bacterial cells can produce a stringy ooze of bacteria streaming from a cut infected plant part placed in water. Single bacterial cells are too small to see without a microscope.

Plant-pathogenic bacteria do not make their own food; they must obtain it from living or dead plant tissue. Nearly all plant-pathogenic bacteria are poor competitors in soil and thus decline rapidly in population without a host. Bacteria enter plants through natural plant openings (such as leaf stomata) and wounds caused by hail, insect feeding, and windblown soil. Spread from plant to plant occurs primarily by wind-driven rain.

The symptoms caused by bacteria include water soaking and leaf lesions. A sign of bacterial disease is bacterial streaming, described earlier in this section.

Viruses

Viruses are another type of plant pathogen. They are extremely small and can be seen only with an electron microscope (Fig. 2.13).

A virus is usually composed of a protein coat surrounding a piece of genetic material. It multiplies by programming infected plant cells to make more virus particles, instead of carrying out normal plant functions. This phenomenon explains why virus-infected plants often exhibit abnormal growth (such as leaf strapping and puckering) and unusual leaf colors and patterns.

Viruses are generally able to survive only within living host cells and require direct transport from infected to healthy plants. The majority of plant viruses are spread by insects (vectors), which transmit these pathogens as they feed on healthy plants. People, nematodes, tools, and machinery can also spread viruses. Sometimes, leaf-to-leaf contact is enough to spread a virus from an infected plant to a healthy plant.

Symptoms of virus diseases include mosaic and mottle patterns on foliage, tissue distortion, and stunted growth.

Nematodes

Nematodes are nonsegmented roundworms that live in soil and water. They are much smaller than earthworms and can be seen only with

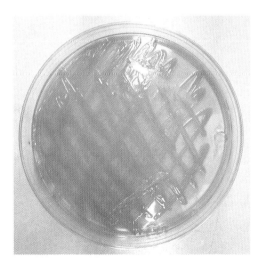

FIG. 2.12. Bacterial growth of the bacterium that causes Goss's wilt.

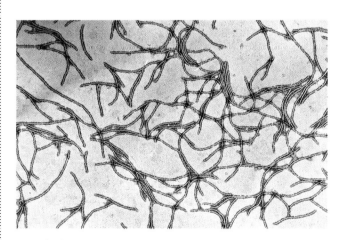

FIG. 2.13. Virus particles.

magnification. Nematodes feed on plants, animals, fungi, and even other nematodes. One acre of a cultivated agricultural field contains hundreds of millions of nematodes.

Plant-parasitic nematodes puncture plant cells with a specialized feeding structure called a stylet. The stylet—which is hardened, needle shaped, and hollow—is used to inject substances into and remove food from plant cells. Plant-parasitic nematodes may invade the plant and feed within plant tissue, or they may feed on the plant from its exterior. Most plant-parasitic nematodes feed on plant roots, interfering with the uptake of water and nutrients (Fig. 2.14). Nematodes often interact with other nematodes and pathogens to injure crops.

A nematode begins its life cycle as an egg; masses of eggs are laid by female nematodes. Juveniles emerge after the eggs hatch, and they molt (shed their body walls) several times before becoming adults, which are able to reproduce.

Symptoms of damage caused by nematodes occur both above and below the ground. Nematode-infected root systems may appear rotted or stunted or have portions destroyed; some nematodes cause root proliferation. Aboveground symptoms include wilting, stunting, yellowing, and loss of plant vigor. These symptoms can be confused with those caused by other diseases and disorders.

The Disease Cycle

The disease cycle is the series of events that occurs as a plant pathogen develops (Fig. 2.15). This concept is similar to that of the life cycle of an insect, which passes through various stages before reaching

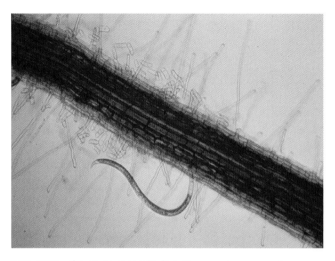

FIG. 2.14. Stunt nematode feeding on a corn root.

FIG. 2.15. Disease cycle of gray leaf spot.

maturity. For many plant diseases, the disease cycle includes these stages:

1. initial production of inoculum
2. dispersal of inoculum to a suitable host
3. penetration of host
4. infection of host
5. colonization of host tissue and incubation
6. development of symptoms
7. initiation and completion of secondary disease cycles (if any)
8. survival of the pathogen (when not in a living host)

Inocula (singular: inoculum) are the forms of pathogens capable of spreading and facilitating host infection. Fungal spores, bacterial cells, and virus particles are all forms of inocula. Primary inoculum is dispersed initially to a host, and secondary inoculum is dispersed from one host to another or from leaf to leaf.

Dispersal is accomplished when wind, water, animals, or people move inoculum. Inoculum can survive in many places, including plant residue, infected seed, insects, and soil. In addition, a single disease can have multiple sources of inoculum. In some cases, inoculum dispersal can be managed by planting pathogen-free seed, cleaning field equipment and tools, reducing vector populations, and minimizing vector access to plants. The spread of inoculum by wind and water may be out of farmers' control, however.

Once inoculum comes in contact with a suitable host, it must penetrate or gain entry into the host. This occurs when the plant surface (or exterior) is successfully breached. Inoculum can enter the host through natural openings and wounds and through direct penetration into host plant tissue. Insects that have fed on infected plant tissue may introduce certain pathogens to other plants they feed on.

Once the host has been penetrated and infection occurs, the pathogen establishes a food or energy relationship with the host.

Colonization occurs as the pathogen develops in or on plant tissue. Depending on the pathogen and the disease, development may involve only a few types of plant tissue and occur only during certain stages of crop development.

After colonization, incubation occurs. The length of the incubation period varies depending on the pathogen and the environmental conditions. Symptoms are not always evident on an infected plant during the incubation process, and if the environment becomes unfavorable for disease development during this process, colonization may halt and symptoms may not materialize. Symptoms typically appear after incubation.

A secondary disease cycle occurs when new inoculum is produced in or on a host. This inoculum can contribute to pathogen spread by infecting surrounding plants or additional parts of the same plant. Some pathogens have only one disease cycle each year, whereas others have two or more.

Plant pathogens must survive during periods that are unfavorable for infection and growth and when living host tissue is not available, and they can accomplish this in a variety of ways (Fig. 2.16). For instance, some fungi survive adverse conditions by forming small, hard structures called sclerotia. Other pathogens, such as viruses, can survive inside insect vectors during the winter or overwinter on alternative plant hosts, such as weeds. Rust fungi survive on living hosts, and spores can be carried by winds each year from geographic areas where corn and/or an alternate host are growing.

Breaking the Disease Cycle

To break the disease cycle, farmers must incorporate management strategies that effectively avoid, reduce, or control disease. As discussed in the following sections, several management practices are recommended for diseases of corn. Often, applying

FIG. 2.16. Many pathogens survive in corn residue.

more than one strategy is necessary for optimal disease management. Before implementing any management strategy, the farmer should consider not only its effectiveness but also any potential economic, environmental, and social impacts.

Hybrid Selection

Hybrid selection is the foundation of disease management. Some hybrids are very susceptible to certain diseases, whereas others may have the genetic ability to resist disease (Fig. 2.17). Resistant hybrids can prevent initial infection and colonization by the pathogen or slow or reduce inoculum production. For example, hybrids with resistance to gray leaf spot may still be infected by the pathogen, but the leaf lesions that develop will be smaller and produce fewer spores than the lesions that develop on susceptible hybrids.

High-Quality Seed

Planting high-quality seed can reduce the occurrence of diseases caused by pathogens that survive or reside in or on seed. Planting high-quality seed may also prevent pathogens from being introduced into new geographic areas.

Cultural Practices

Cultural practices are nonpesticide-based tactics that are implemented to minimize the risk of disease. Some cultural practices improve plant health and optimize the growing environment for the crop. For example, practices such as planting at the appropriate seeding rate and maintaining adequate soil fertility limit the stress on corn plants or make the environment less conducive for disease development.

A few common cultural practices are described in the following sections.

Crop Rotation. Planting a nonhost crop in a field denies the pathogen access to a suitable host and prevents the population from increasing. This provides time for the pathogen inoculum level to diminish as crop residue decomposes. The inoculum level diminishes because saprophytes often outcompete disease-causing organisms in the crop residue for nutrients. Pathogens may even be suppressed or destroyed by antagonistic organisms in the soil.

The risk of some diseases developing can increase if the rotational crop or the crop in a nearby field is also susceptible to a particular pathogen. Examples of corn diseases that have an increased risk of developing based on the previous crop include the following:

- *Previous crop soybean:* Charcoal rot
- *Previous crop sorghum:* Head smut, sorghum downy mildew
- *Previous crop corn:* Many pathogens survive the winter in corn residue, which means many diseases are more severe when corn follows corn in a field.

Some pathogens spread to corn from crops in neighboring fields. Diseases that have a higher risk of developing if corn is planted close to a particular crop include the following:

- *Planted close to sorghum:* Sorghum downy mildew
- *Planted close to wheat:* Gibberella ear rot, high plains disease

Planting and Harvest Dates. Adjusting planting and harvest dates may help avoid the presence of pathogens and losses caused by disease. For example, seedling blights may not be problematic when corn is planted later in the season, after soils have warmed. However, delayed planting may increase the risk of other diseases and reduce the yield potential.

FIG. 2.17. Corn hybrid susceptible to Goss's wilt (right), compared with a hybrid with genetic resistance to this disease (left).

Harvest becomes more difficult when stalk rots cause corn to lodge (Fig. 2.18). This problem can be avoided by harvesting severely diseased fields first, before other fields. Delaying harvest may also allow some pathogens, such as those that cause ear molds, to increase late in the season.

Tillage. Tillage is an effective disease management tool. Soil surface residue, which can harbor pathogen inoculum, can be buried using tillage, allowing for quicker decomposition and reduced pathogen survival. Furthermore, burying the residue may remove the pathogen from direct contact with the host crop. Certain corn diseases can be more problematic when infested residue is present.

Soils are typically wetter and cooler for longer periods when covered by residue, which can cause an increased incidence of seedling disease in a field with minimal tillage. However, tillage also exposes soil to erosion, which can lead to soil degradation. Thus, it is important to consider both the positive and negative effects of tillage before using it for disease management.

Insect Management

Managing insects can reduce some insect-transmitted diseases. Some fungal spores can be carried on insect bodies, and viruses and bacteria can be transported inside insects. For instance, the corn flea beetle can carry the bacterium that causes Stewart's disease (*Pantoea stewartii*) and introduce it to corn via feeding. Wounding by insects can create entry points for pathogens. Ear rots and mycotoxin-contaminated kernels are typically found at higher levels on ears on which insect feeding has occurred. After corn stalk borers burrow into plants, pathogens can gain access through the wounds and cause stalk rot. An integrated pest management plan should be used when deciding to reduce insect vectors of plant pathogens.

Weed Management

Not only do weeds compete with crops, but they are also hosts of certain pathogens. *Maize dwarf mosaic virus* overwinters in johnsongrass and is spread by aphids when they feed on infected johnsongrass and then on corn. The presence

FIG. 2.18. The timely harvest of a field is important to prevent lodging caused by stalk rots.

of additional weed hosts in a field can mean the pathogen produces a greater quantity of inoculum because more host plants are present. Weeds may also create disease-conducive microclimates that are favorable for spore production (Fig. 2.19).

Weeds that are present before or during the growing season can be conducive to the development of many diseases, including the following: charcoal rot, crazy top, Goss's wilt, holcus leaf spot, maize chlorotic dwarf, maize chlorotic mottle, maize dwarf mosaic, Rhizoctonia crown and brace root rot, sorghum downy mildew, and Stewart's disease. The presence of weeds can also enhance the development of diseases caused by nematodes, including root-lesion, sting, and needle nematodes.

Fungicides

Fungicides are pesticides used to manage fungi. These products can be applied as seed treatments, in furrow, or as foliar sprays. Seed treatments and in-furrow applications protect young plants from soilborne pathogens; most hybrid corn grown in the United States and Canada receives a fungicide seed treatment of some kind (Fig. 2.20). Foliar applications can prevent spore germination and/or fungal growth on plants, depending on the chemical group or groups contained in the fungicide.

Applying fungicides is most effective before disease is established (preventively) and/or when the risk for disease is high. Fungicide applications are most successful when used in tandem with other management practices.

Nematicides

Nematicides are pesticides used to manage nematodes. Only a few products are labeled for use on corn, and they include seed treatments and soil

FIG. 2.20. Pesticide-treated corn seed.

FIG. 2.19. A weedy cornfield can create conditions favorable for disease.

treatments. Because nematode damage often occurs in patches (based on population density), fieldwide application of a nematicide may not be necessary or economical. Before a nematicide is applied, soil samples should be tested to determine the species and population of nematode.

NONINFECTIOUS DISORDERS

Plant injuries caused by nonliving agents are known as noninfectious disorders or abiotic disorders. These disorders reduce plant growth and development in a variety of ways and can be physical or chemical in nature. Noninfectious disorders will not spread to other plants, although many plants in one area may all display the same symptoms. These disorders can make plants more susceptible to infectious diseases.

Noninfectious disorders can be caused by many factors, including weather and climate conditions such as temperature extremes, flooding, drought, wind, hail, and lack of light (Fig. 2.21). Chemicals, nutritional deficiencies, and mechanical damage can also cause noninfectious disorders.

Symptoms of noninfectious disorders vary but can include wilting, yellowing, and stunting, as well as damaged, dead, and deformed tissue. Some of the symptoms of noninfectious disorders can be mistaken for those of infectious diseases. The following sections identify clues that can

be used to determine if symptoms are the result of a noninfectious disorder or caused by a plant pathogen.

Field Patterns

A pattern in the field may indicate that symptoms have resulted from a noninfectious disorder (Fig. 2.22). For example, if a spray boom applying a chemical in a field overlapped a few rows that had already received an application, symptoms

FIG. 2.22. A pattern in a cornfield can indicate an abiotic issue. This corn has damage on the older leaves but not the younger leaves, indicating that herbicide drift occurred.

FIG. 2.21. (A) Hail damage and **(B)** drought stress are among the factors that can cause noninfectious disorders.

may occur in a straight line down the field. The appearance of stunted plants at low spots in a field may be attributed to flooding.

Timing

Symptoms that result from noninfectious disorders appear after certain events take place. Farmers should check pesticide application and weather records to see what occurred prior to symptom expression. For instance, drift from an herbicide application to an adjacent field may have occurred after spraying on a windy day, or a strong storm may have caused lodged stalks and tattered leaves.

Other Plants

Other species of plants in the area should be checked. If more than one species of plant shows a similar injury but no continued progression of damage, then a noninfectious disorder may be the cause.

THE CORN PLANT

Understanding the stages of corn development can help to maximize crop yields, because certain management issues must be considered at particular stages. Additionally, the corn plant is susceptible to particular diseases at certain developmental stages. Knowing the plant's developmental stages can help farmers be aware of what problems might occur throughout the growing season. Some management strategies may have the greatest impact when used at the appropriate developmental stages.

Stages of Development

Corn development proceeds through both vegetative stages and reproductive stages (Fig. 2.23). When 50% or more of the plants in a field have reached a particular stage, the field is classified as being at that stage. Multiple growth-staging methods are available for determining corn growth stages, including the horizontal or droopy leaf method used by crop insurance adjustors, among others. The following description of stages is based on the leaf collar method, in which vegetative stages are defined according to the presence of leaf collars and reproductive stages are defined according to kernel development.

Vegetative Stages

VE: The shoot (coleoptile) emerges from the soil.

V1: The collar becomes visible on the lowest leaf. Every leaf on the plant is pointed except this one, which has a rounded tip. This stage occurs approximately 3–4 days after emergence.

V2: The collars are visible on the bottom two leaves. This stage occurs approximately 7–10 days after emergence.

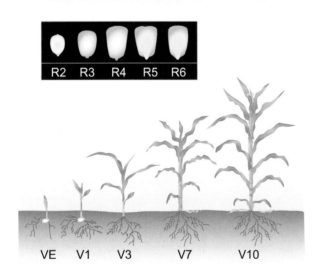
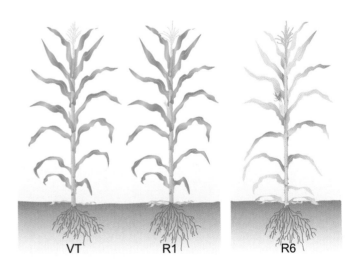

FIG. 2.23. Stages of corn development. (V = vegetative; R = reproductive.)

V(n): The collars are visible on *n*th number of leaves; the majority of hybrids in the U.S. Corn Belt will have 19–20 leaves when fully grown.

VT: The entire tassel has emerged, regardless of whether it is shedding pollen. This is the final vegetative stage.

Reproductive Stages

R1: Silk—One or more silks become visible beyond the husk leaves.

R2: Blister—Kernels have a blisterlike appearance, with clear liquid on the interior and an ivory exterior. This stage occurs approximately 10–14 days after silking.

R3: Milk—The interiors of kernels are milklike and translucent white, and the exteriors are yellow. This stage occurs approximately 18–22 days after silking.

R4: Dough—The interiors of kernels are doughlike. This stage occurs approximately 24–28 days after silking.

R5: Dent—A visible dent forms on the top of each kernel as the starch level increases and the moisture level decreases. The "milk" line moves down.

R6: Physiological maturity—Corn has reached maturity, and its dry matter content has been determined. A black layer becomes visible on the interior of the kernel near the tip.

Effects of Stress at Key Developmental Stages

Certain diseases and disorders can be more or less problematic at various developmental stages of the corn plant:

- The growing point of the corn plant remains belowground until V6. Injury to the plant before this growth stage (such as frost damage) may stall growth and development for a few days; however, the plant may recover (Fig. 2.24).
- The potential number of ear shoots is determined by V5. From V6 until about V8, the number of rows of kernels and the number of kernels per row are established. The potential number of kernels per row can be affected by stresses until silking. While the number of kernels per row

and the ear size are determined genetically, the number of rows of kernels and the number of kernels per ear can be reduced by plant stress caused by disease, environment, and production practices during stages V6 through V8.

- Silking begins at R1 and must be synchronized with pollen shed for successful pollination. Drought stress and excessive rainfall may cause poor pollen shed or delayed silk emergence, resulting in poor pollination because of asynchrony between silk and pollen production.
- During R2 and R3, kernels can be aborted in response to severe stress. Kernel abortion typically begins at the ear tip (Fig. 2.25). Stress at these stages can result not only in aborted kernels but also in reduction of the sizes of individual kernels.

FIG. 2.24. Plants injured before stage V6 may recover.

FIG. 2.25. Kernel abortion at the ear tips.

- Kernel starch accumulation increases at R4 and R5, as the moisture level in the kernel is reduced. Kernel weight can decrease, resulting in small, shriveled kernels.
- After plants reach maturity at R6, stress no longer affects kernel number, size, or weight. However, poor plant health may result in stalk lodging, ear drop, or ear injury.

Scouting for Diseases of Corn

Seedling, foliar, stalk, and ear diseases affect corn plants in a variety of ways and at different times during the growing season. Knowing how to scout for these various types of disease can help to determine the extent of injury that is occurring or has already taken place and to decide on the proper management steps.

Seedling Diseases

- Seedling diseases are usually more prevalent in early planted and/or minimum-tilled fields. These diseases are also more likely to occur if soil conditions at or soon after planting were wet and cold (less than 60°F [15°C]).
- Scouting should occur from VE to V6.
- The entire field should be scouted. The focus should be on low-lying areas, wet spots, and areas with large amounts of surface residue (Fig. 2.26).

- Plants should be examined for leaf scorch, wilting, and seedling death. Symptomatic plants should be carefully dug up, and the mesocotyl, seminal root system, and nodal roots (if present) should be examined for rotting.
- Seedling diseases can appear similar to other biotic and abiotic stresses. Laboratory diagnosis may be needed to determine the exact causes of some symptoms.
- How much stand loss has occurred should be determined by taking several counts across the field. The decision to replant will depend on the remaining plant stand, as well as timing and economics (that is, cost of seed, field activity, yield loss from replanting at a later date).

Foliar Diseases

- Many foliar diseases are more prevalent when infected corn residue is present in the field (Fig. 2.27).
- Scouting for the majority of foliar diseases should occur just before VT through R4.
- Areas throughout the field should be scouted, and at least 100 leaves per field should be examined. It is important to assess the entire field.
- Leaves should be examined in the lower, middle, and upper canopies. Some diseases start on the lower leaves and symptoms progress up,

FIG. 2.26. Ponding increases the risk for seedling disease.

FIG. 2.27. Corn planted in corn residue is at greater risk for developing disease.

whereas symptoms of other diseases appear first on the upper or middle leaves. Farmers should pay special attention to symptoms on the ear leaf and above, because photosynthesis in these leaves contributes to grain fill.

- Properly identifying foliar diseases is critical in determining which management practices to implement.

Stalk Rots

- Corn plants stressed during the grain-filling stages will cannibalize stalk tissue and remobilize carbohydrates from the stalk to the ears to complete grain fill. This process weakens the stalk and makes it more vulnerable to pathogens.
- Usually, the prevalence of stalk rot is greater when infested corn residue is present and when other stresses that reduce photosynthesis (such as foliar disease) are present. Diseases and injuries that reduce the photosynthetic area on leaf tissue can make plants more susceptible to stalk rot, because plants have fewer photosynthates to fill ears and support stalks and roots.
- Scouting for most stalk rots should occur from R5 through R6; however, premature plant death resulting from Pythium or bacterial stalk rot can occur as early as the midvegetative stages and through R5.

- Areas throughout the field should be scouted, and at least 100 plants per field should be examined. It is important to assess the entire field.
- If the first to the third internodes above the soil can be crushed easily when pinched, stalk rot is likely developing (Fig. 2.28). Inner symptoms can be observed by splitting the stalk in half.
- Fields should be harvested early when stalk rot affects more than 10% of the plants. Farmers should consider the potential ear drop or grain loss that results from stalk lodging, as well as additional costs for drying grain that has been harvested early.

Ear Rots

- Ear rots and mycotoxins are usually more prevalent in fields that have experienced damage from insects, birds, or hail (Fig. 2.29) and/or minimally tilled fields and continuous corn production.
- Although the fungi that cause ear rots infect plants at or after silking (R1), scouting for most ear rots should occur from R5 to R6, when symptoms are most evident. Scouting should begin at R4 for Diplodia ear rot.
- Ears should be checked in several locations throughout the field, and at least 100 ears should be examined per field. The entire ear should be examined, because ear rot fungi can infect other areas of the ear besides the tip.

FIG. 2.28. Example of performing the pinch test to assess stalk rot damage.

FIG. 2.29. Hail damage on ears of corn.

- Fields should be harvested early when ear rot affects 10% or more of the plants, especially if the ear rot pathogen produces mycotoxins.
- Grain affected by ear rots should be stored separately from unaffected grain, dried to 15% moisture, and cooled quickly for storage. Bins that contain moldy or mycotoxin-affected grain should be checked frequently to ensure that the bin moisture does not exceed 15% and that the temperature of the grain does not increase.
- Feeding moldy or mycotoxin-contaminated grain to livestock can cause health issues in the animals. Moldy grain should be tested for the presence of mycotoxins before it is fed to animals.

Corn Diseases and Disorders

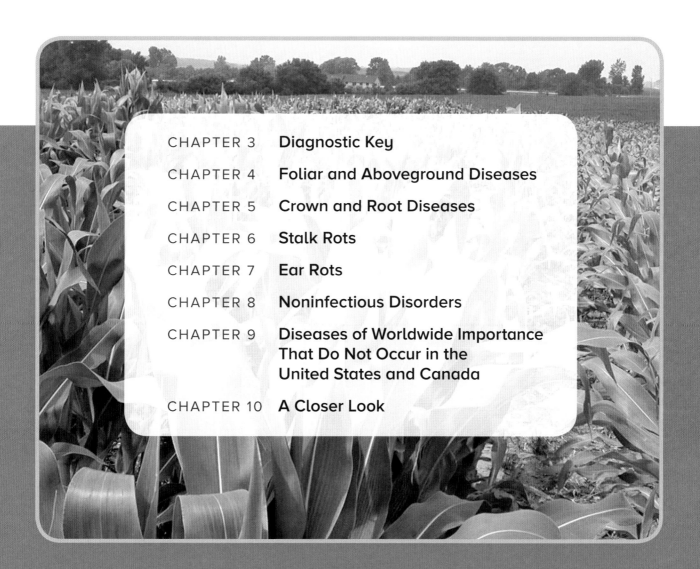

CHAPTER 3

Diagnostic Key

Diagnosing plant disease involves considerable information gathering. Scouting should begin even before you set foot into the field. One of your first steps should be to collect information about the field, such as crop rotation practices, previous disease history, and hybrid susceptibility to disease. In addition, you should learn about past and current weather conditions (Fig. 3.1). Equipping yourself with this knowledge will help you narrow down the list of potential diseases and disorders.

The diagnostic process will be easier if you consider specific factors such as when the disease has developed, how it is distributed in the field or on the plant, what weather conditions have recently occurred, and what crop management practices have been applied. You should also keep in mind that certain symptoms and signs are generally specific to one disease or group of diseases. Doing so will

help you further narrow down the possibilities for diagnosis.

To assist you in gathering all of this information, the following sections outline the most common diseases that develop under certain field conditions, under specific weather conditions, during given timeframes, and according to certain distributions in the field and that display certain symptoms and signs. Use the green key words to help arrive at a correct diagnosis. Diseases associated with key words are more likely to occur under the listed conditions, but not all the diseases associated with a particular key word may be listed.

Also look for these key words in the discussions of specific diseases throughout Chapters 4 through 9. Relevant key words are provided in the section Diagnostic Key Words, which ends the discussion of each disease.

FIG. 3.1. Weather conditions can influence disease diagnosis.

FIELD CONDITIONS

Field conditions will affect the type of disease present.

> **Corn planted in** sandy soils: Aspergillus ear rot, drought, other nematodes, Rhizoctonia crown and brace root rot, root-lesion nematode, sting and needle nematodes

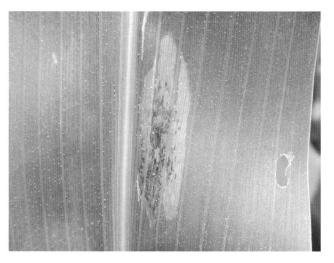

FIG. 3.2. Development of Goss's wilt near a leaf wound.

> **Corn plants with** wounding **(recent storm or insect injury):** Aspergillus ear rot, bacterial stalk rot, buggy-whipping, Cladosporium ear rot, common smut, Fusarium ear rot, Goss's wilt, greensnap, holcus leaf spot, insect injury, lightning damage, Nigrospora ear rot, Penicillium ear rot, Trichoderma ear rot (Fig. 3.2)

WEATHER CONDITIONS

Weather conditions affect how different diseases and disorders develop. As indicated in the previous section, weather is a factor in some of the diseases related to particular field conditions. Another way to determine which diseases might be more prevalent under certain conditions is to compare the general weather conditions in the current season with the 30-year average in a given region.

> **Symptoms may be more severe under exceptionally** dry **conditions:** Aspergillus ear rot, charcoal rot, common smut, drought, Fusarium ear rot, Fusarium stalk rot, head smut, Nigrospora ear rot, other nematodes, Stewart's disease (Fig. 3.3)

FIG. 3.3. Symptoms of drought stress on corn plants.

> **Wet weather (dew, free moisture, humidity) favors many diseases:** anthracnose leaf blight, anthracnose stalk rot, bacterial stalk rot, banded leaf and sheath blight, Cladosporium ear rot, common rust, crazy top, Diplodia ear rot, Diplodia leaf streak, eyespot, flooding, Fusarium crown and root rot, Gibberella ear rot, Gibberella stalk rot (during fall), Goss's wilt, gray leaf spot, holcus leaf spot, northern corn leaf blight, northern corn leaf spot, Penicillium ear rot, Physoderma brown spot and stalk rot, Pythium seedling blight and root rot, Pythium stalk rot, Rhizoctonia crown and brace root rot, sorghum downy mildew, southern corn leaf blight, southern rust, sting and needle nematodes

> **Ponding/Wet soils:** anthracnose stalk rot, bacterial stalk rot, crazy top, flooding, Fusarium crown and root rot, Physoderma stalk rot, Pythium seedling blight and root rot, Pythium stalk rot, Rhizoctonia crown and brace root rot (Fig. 3.4)

> **Cool (70s°F [20–25°C]) daytime air temperatures during the growing season:** common rust, eyespot, Gibberella ear rot, northern corn leaf spot (race 3), Pythium seedling blight and root rot

> **Warm (80s+°F [26–30°C]) daytime air temperatures during the growing season:** anthracnose leaf blight, anthracnose stalk rot, Aspergillus ear rot, bacterial stalk rot, banded leaf and sheath blight, charcoal rot, common smut, Diplodia leaf streak, Fusarium ear rot, Fusarium stalk rot, Gibberella stalk rot, Goss's wilt, gray leaf spot, head smut, high temperatures, holcus leaf spot, maize dwarf mosaic, northern corn leaf spot (race 2), other nematodes, Physoderma brown spot and stalk rot, Pythium stalk rot, sorghum downy mildew, southern corn leaf blight, southern rust

DISEASE TIMELINE AND FIELD DISTRIBUTION

After you have gathered information regarding field and weather conditions, consider the time of year and where symptoms occur in the field and on the corn plant. These factors can be used to further narrow the diagnostic possibilities. In Table 3.1, highlighted growth stages within a given disease indicate the growth stages in which this disease is most likely to be observed. As shown in the table, diseases are considered to be **early season** (VE to V4), **midseason** (V8–R2), and **late season** (R3–R6).

> **Symptoms on plants throughout the field (fieldwide):** anthracnose leaf blight (lower canopy), common rust (middle to upper canopy), eyespot (lower canopy early in the season, upper canopy later), frost damage, Goss's wilt (leaf blight; middle to upper canopy), gray leaf spot (lower canopy early in the season), hail damage, holcus leaf spot, northern corn leaf blight, northern corn leaf spot (lower canopy), Physoderma brown spot (middle canopy), soil crusting, southern corn leaf blight, southern rust (middle to upper canopy), Stewart's disease (leaf blight)

> **Localized or patchy symptoms:** anthracnose stalk rot, charcoal rot, corn stunt, Diplodia leaf streak, Diplodia stalk rot, Fusarium crown and root rot, Fusarium stalk rot, Gibberella stalk rot, lesion mimic, lightning damage, maize bushy stunt, maize chlorotic dwarf, maize chlorotic mottle, maize dwarf mosaic, other nematodes, Pythium seedling blight and root rot, Rhizoctonia crown and brace root rot, root-lesion nematode, sting and needle nematodes (Fig. 3.5 on page 30)

FIG. 3.4. Ponding in a cornfield.

TABLE 3.1. Growth stages at which diseases are most likely to be observed.

Diagnostic Key

	VE	V2	V4	V8	V12	VT	R1	R2	R3	R4	R5	R6	Seed
	Early Season			Midseason					Late Season				
Foliar Diseases													
Anthracnose leaf blight		●	●										
Banded leaf and sheath blight				●	●	●	●	●	●	●	●	●	
Common rust					●	●	●	●	●	●			
Common smut		●	●	●	●	●	●	●	●	●	●	●	
Corn stunt				●	●	●	●	●	●	●	●		
Crazy top				●	●	●	●	●					
Diplodia leaf streak						●	●	●	●	●	●		
Eyespot					●	●	●	●	●	●	●		
Goss's wilt			●	●	●	●	●	●	●	●	●		
Gray leaf spot					●	●	●	●	●	●	●		
Head smut								●	●	●	●	●	
Holcus leaf spot		●	●	●	●	●	●	●	●	●	●		
Maize bushy stunt		●	●	●	●	●	●	●	●	●	●	●	
Maize chlorotic dwarf		●	●	●	●	●	●	●	●	●	●	●	
Maize chlorotic mottle		●	●	●	●	●	●	●	●	●	●	●	
Maize dwarf mosaic		●	●	●	●	●	●	●	●	●	●	●	
Northern corn leaf blight				●	●	●	●	●	●	●	●		
Northern corn leaf spot					●	●	●	●	●	●	●		
Physoderma brown spot and stalk rot				●	●	●	●	●	●	●	●		
Sorghum downy mildew		●	●	●	●	●	●	●	●	●	●	●	
Southern corn leaf blight				●	●	●	●	●	●	●	●		
Southern rust				●	●	●	●	●	●	●	●		
Stewart's disease		●	●	●	●	●	●	●	●	●	●	●	
Other viruses		●	●	●	●	●	●	●	●	●	●	●	
Crown and Root Diseases													
Fusarium crown and root rot							●	●	●	●	●	●	●
Pythium seedling blight and root rot	●	●	●										
Red root rot												●	
Rhizoctonia crown and brace root rot	●	●	●							●	●	●	
Root-lesion nematode			●	●	●	●	●	●	●	●	●	●	
Sting and needle nematodes			●	●	●	●	●	●	●	●	●	●	●
Others (lance, root-knot, stubby-root)			●	●	●	●	●	●	●	●	●	●	

TABLE 3.1. *Continued*

	VE	V2	V4	V8	V12	VT	R1	R2	R3	R4	R5	R6	Seed
	Early Season			Midseason					Late Season				
Stalk Rots													
Bacterial stalk rot		•	•	•	•	•	•	•	•	•	•	•	
Pythium stalk rot		•	•	•	•	•	•	•	•	•	•	•	
All other stalk rots											•	•	
Ear Rots													
Ear rots										•	•	•	•
Other													
Magnesium deficiency	•	•	•	•	•	•	•	•	•	•	•		
Nitrogen deficiency			•	•	•	•	•	•	•	•	•	•	
Potassium deficiency				•	•	•	•	•	•	•	•	•	
Sulfur deficiency			•	•	•	•	•	•	•	•	•	•	
Zinc deficiency	•	•	•										
Fertilizer injury	•	•	•										
Herbicide injury	•	•	•	•	•			•	•	•		•	
Crop additive injury			•	•		•		•			•		
Soil crusting	•	•											
Frost damage	•	•								•	•	•	
Lesion mimic			•	•	•	•	•	•	•	•	•	•	
Purple leaf sheath								•	•	•	•	•	
Flooding	•	•	•	•	•	•	•	•	•	•	•	•	
Drought	•	•	•	•	•	•	•	•	•	•	•	•	
Hail damage	•	•	•	•	•	•	•	•	•	•	•	•	
High temperatures						•	•	•	•	•	•	•	
Stalk lodging												•	
Greensnap			•	•	•	•							
Lightning damage		•	•	•	•	•	•	•	•	•	•		
Buggy-whipping			•	•	•								
Insect injury	•	•	•	•	•	•	•	•	•	•	•	•	•
Fijiviruses		•	•	•	•	•	•	•	•	•	•	•	
Maize streak			•	•	•	•	•	•	•	•	•	•	
Late wilt							•	•	•	•	•	•	
Asian downy mildews			•	•	•	•	•	•	•	•	•	•	

FIG. 3.5. Symptom patterns in a cornfield.

> **Single, scattered plants with symptoms:** anthracnose stalk rot (top dieback, upper canopy), bacterial stalk rot, buggy-whipping, common smut, crazy top, Diplodia ear rot, Goss's wilt, head smut, lesion mimic, Pythium stalk rot, Stewart's disease (wilt), Trichoderma ear rot

SYMPTOMS AND SIGNS

Finally, you should observe the symptoms and signs present on the plants. These indicators will provide the best clues as to what disease or disorder is present in the field. However, many diseases have similar symptoms and signs, which is why considering other factors—such as weather and field history—is an important part of the diagnostic process.

General Plant Symptoms and Signs

> **Slow or poor emergence (dig up seeds in spots with inconsistent emergence to inspect more closely):** fertilizer injury, flooding, frost damage, Fusarium crown and root rot, herbicide injury, insect injury, Pythium seedling blight and root rot, soil crusting (Fig. 3.6)

> **Stunting of plants (compared with healthy plants in the field):** Asian downy mildews, common smut, corn stunt, crazy top, fijiviruses, Fusarium crown and root rot, head smut, high plains disease,

FIG. 3.6. Uneven emergence of corn plants.

FIG. 3.7. Severely stunted corn plants.

maize bushy stunt, maize chlorotic dwarf, maize chlorotic mottle, maize dwarf mosaic, maize streak, other nematodes, Rhizoctonia crown and brace root rot, root-lesion nematode, sorghum downy mildew, Stewart's disease, sting and needle nematodes (Fig. 3.7)

> **Tillering:** Asian downy mildews, corn stunt, crazy top, head smut, insect injury, maize bushy stunt, maize dwarf mosaic, Stewart's disease

> **Galls on plant tissue:** common smut (anywhere on plant), fijiviruses, head smut (tassels and ears) (Fig. 3.8)

> **Tissue distortion:** Asian downy mildews, buggy-whipping, corn stunt (ear and shoot proliferation), crazy top (tassel, ear, and ear shoot proliferation; narrow leaves), fijiviruses, head smut (leaflike proliferations on tassel and ear), herbicide injury, maize bushy stunt (ear, shoot, and leaf proliferation; short leaves), maize chlorotic dwarf (leaf distortion, vein swelling), maize chlorotic mottle (deformed ears, tassel stunting), sorghum downy mildew (narrow leaves)

> **Wilting of plant:** bacterial stalk rot, drought, Fusarium crown and root rot, Fusarium stalk rot, Gibberella stalk rot, Goss's wilt, late wilt, Pythium root rot, red root rot, Stewart's disease, sting and needle nematodes

> **Lodging:** anthracnose stalk rot, bacterial stalk rot (plant stays green), charcoal rot, common smut, Diplodia stalk rot, Fusarium stalk rot, Gibberella stalk rot, Goss's wilt, insect injury, Physoderma stalk rot, Pythium stalk rot (plant stays green), red root rot, Rhizoctonia crown and brace root rot, stalk lodging (Fig. 3.9)

> **Death of mature plants:** anthracnose stalk rot (top dieback), Asian downy mildews, bacterial stalk rot, banded leaf and sheath blight, charcoal rot, corn lethal necrosis, corn stunt, Diplodia stalk rot, drought, eyespot, flooding, Fusarium crown and root rot, Fusarium stalk rot, Gibberella stalk rot, gray leaf spot, late wilt, lightning damage, maize bushy stunt, maize chlorotic mottle, northern corn leaf blight, northern corn leaf spot, Pythium stalk rot, red root rot, Stewart's disease (Fig. 3.10)

FIG. 3.8. Galls caused by head smut.

FIG. 3.9. Lodged corn plants.

FIG. 3.10. Premature death of a corn plant.

> **Signs of fungal infection:** anthracnose stalk rot (top dieback), Aspergillus ear rot, banded leaf and sheath blight, charcoal rot, Cladosporium ear rot, common rust, common smut, Diplodia ear rot, Diplodia leaf streak, Diplodia stalk rot, Fusarium ear rot, Gibberella ear rot, Gibberella stalk rot, head smut, Nigrospora ear rot, Penicillium ear rot, southern rust, Trichoderma ear rot (Fig. 3.11)

Symptoms and Signs on Specific Plant Tissues

Roots and Crowns

Most root diseases have similar symptoms, so it is often hard to diagnose a specific root disease based solely on symptoms. In most cases, symptoms on roots include general rotting, reduced root size, and lesions.

> **Root and crown symptoms/signs:** Fusarium crown and root rot (mesocotyl firm or shriveled), maize bushy stunt, other nematodes (root pruning, swelling, galls, fibrous roots), Pythium seedling blight and root rot (soft rot, root surface peels off), red root rot (reddish, shriveling can occur),

FIG. 3.11. Mycelial mat on an ear of corn.

Rhizoctonia crown and brace root rot (mesocotyl firm and slightly collapsed), root-lesion nematode (root pruning), sting and needle nematodes (root pruning, swelling, bottle brush roots) (Fig. 3.12)

Stalks

> **Stalk symptoms/signs:** anthracnose stalk rot (top dieback), bacterial stalk rot, banded leaf and sheath blight, charcoal rot, common rust, Diplodia stalk rot, Fusarium stalk rot, Gibberella stalk rot, Goss's wilt, late wilt, Physoderma brown spot and stalk rot, Pythium stalk rot, red root rot, southern corn leaf blight, southern rust, Stewart's disease

> **Lesions or blotches on stalk (stalk lesions):** anthracnose stalk rot (top dieback, rind blackening and black lesions beneath leaf and sheath blight at plant top), banded leaf and sheath blight, charcoal rot (silvery gray), common rust (reddish with pustules), Diplodia stalk rot (black pycnidia at lower internodes and white mold), Fusarium stalk rot (straw-colored and brown streaks at lower internodes), Gibberella stalk rot (straw-colored and dark streaks at lower internodes and small, round, bluish-black bodies), Physoderma brown spot and stalk rot, southern corn leaf blight (race T), southern rust (orange with pustules) (Fig. 3.13)

> **Discoloration, shredding, or rotting of stalk interior (rotting stalk interior):** anthracnose stalk rot, bacterial stalk rot (with strong odor), charcoal rot (vascular tissue granular and gray), Diplodia stalk rot (initiated at ear), Fusarium stalk rot

FIG. 3.12. Lesions on corn roots.

(pale pink to salmon), Gibberella stalk rot (light pink to red), Goss's wilt (orange/brown vascular tissue), late wilt, Pythium stalk rot (slimy, water-soaked decay), Stewart's disease (dead tissue and cavities) (Fig. 3.14)

Ears/Kernels

〉 **Ears/Kernels with symptoms or signs:** Aspergillus ear rot, Cladosporium ear rot, corn lethal necrosis, corn stunt, crazy top, Diplodia ear rot, drought, frost damage, Fusarium ear rot, Gibberella ear rot, hail damage, insect injury, maize chlorotic mottle, maize dwarf mosaic, Nigrospora ear rot, Penicillium ear rot, sorghum downy mildew, Trichoderma ear rot (Fig. 3.15)

〉 **Mold growth on ears/kernels (ear mold):** Aspergillus ear rot (olive green and powdery on ear or at point of insect injury), Cladosporium ear rot (dark green and fuzzy on whole ear, at base, or with injury), Diplodia ear rot (white mold on whole ear, base of ear, ear shank), Fusarium ear rot (white to purple on scattered/clustered spots on ear), Gibberella ear rot (red or pink on whole ear or ear tip), Nigrospora ear rot (gray to black at base of ear), Penicillium ear rot (green, blue-green, or denim-blue powdery growth at ear tip or associated with insect injury), Trichoderma ear rot (dark green or blue on whole ear)

〉 **Kernel discoloration:** Cladosporium ear rot, Fusarium ear rot, Nigrospora ear rot, Penicillium ear rot

FIG. 3.13. Anthracnose lesions on corn stalks.

FIG. 3.14. Shredded pith inside a corn stalk.

FIG. 3.15. Signs of Fusarium ear rot.

> **Barren ears/Abnormal seed set (abnormal ears):** corn lethal necrosis, corn stunt, crazy top, insect injury, maize chlorotic mottle, maize dwarf mosaic, sorghum downy mildew. Various ear abnormalities can occur, including tip dieback, arrested ears, zipper ears, ear pinching, and nubbin ears. Abnormal ears can be caused by multiple factors, including drought, foliar disease, nutrient deficiency, herbicide or crop additives, and poor pollination (Fig. 3.16).

> **Lightweight/Chaffy ears:** Diplodia ear rot, drought, frost damage, hail damage (at R4–5), Nigrospora ear rot, premature plant death from foliar disease, potassium deficiency

> **Husk/Silk stuck to ear:** Diplodia ear rot, Gibberella ear rot

Leaves

> **Leaves with symptoms or signs:** anthracnose leaf blight, Asian downy mildews, banded leaf and sheath blight, common rust, corn lethal necrosis, corn stunt, crazy top, crop additive injury, Diplodia leaf streak, drought, eyespot, fertilizer injury, fijiviruses, flooding, Goss's wilt (leaf blight), gray leaf spot, herbicide injury, high plains disease, high temperatures, holcus leaf spot, insect injury, lesion mimic, maize bushy stunt, maize chlorotic dwarf, maize chlorotic mottle, maize dwarf mosaic, maize streak, northern corn leaf blight, northern corn leaf spot, nutrient deficiencies, Physoderma brown spot, purple leaf sheath, sorghum downy mildew, southern corn leaf blight, southern rust, Stewart's disease

> **Lesions:** anthracnose leaf blight (brown with dark margins), banded leaf and sheath blight (gray/brown bands), common rust (reddish/brown with pustules on both leaf surfaces), Diplodia leaf streak (tan with dark spots), eyespot (greenish/yellow with halo and dark margins, clustered), Goss's wilt (leaf blight; gray/green with wavy margins, dark spots or "freckles," exudate), gray leaf spot (tan halos in early stages, between veins), herbicide injury, holcus leaf spot (greenish/yellow then tan with dark margins), northern corn leaf blight (tan with dark spots), northern corn leaf spot (brown with dark margins), Physoderma brown spot (brown on midrib, greenish/yellow on leaf, clustered), sorghum downy mildew (greenish/yellow then brown, can have fluffy white growth), southern corn leaf blight (tan with dark margins), southern rust (orange with pustules, mostly on upper surfaces, clustered), Stewart's disease (greenish/yellow then brown with wavy margins). Some diseases cause lesions to appear in different parts of the plant canopy (Fig. 3.17).

> **Lower canopy:** anthracnose leaf blight, eyespot (early in season), gray leaf spot, northern corn leaf blight, northern corn leaf spot

FIG. 3.16. Abnormal ears.

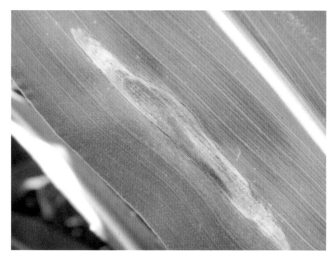

FIG. 3.17. Foliar lesion, caused by northern corn leaf blight.

> **Middle canopy:** common rust, Goss's wilt (leaf blight), Physoderma brown spot, southern rust

> **Upper canopy:** common rust, eyespot (later in season), Goss's wilt (leaf blight), southern rust

> **Some diseases cause leaf discoloration, not necessarily appearing as lesions:** Asian downy mildews (streaks), corn lethal necrosis, corn stunt (yellow/green stripes), crazy top (yellow/green stripes), crop additive injury (spotting or stippling), fertilizer injury, fijiviruses (yellow stripes), herbicide injury, high plains disease (long, red streaks), insect injury, lesion mimic, magnesium deficiency (stripes on outer edges, beading), maize bushy stunt (reddish tips), maize chlorotic dwarf (vein discoloration and yellow/green stripes), maize chlorotic mottle (yellow/green stripes, mottling), maize dwarf mosaic (yellow/green stripes), maize streak (yellow spots growing into streaks), nitrogen deficiency (V-shaped yellowing), potassium deficiency (margins inward), purple leaf sheath, sorghum downy mildew (white stripes), sulfur deficiency (light-green/yellow stripes), zinc deficiency (yellow stripes) (Fig. 3.18)

> **Leaf margins dead:** drought, flooding, Goss's wilt, fertilizer injury, high temperatures, potassium deficiency (Fig. 3.19)

FIG. 3.18. Mosaic symptoms on leaves, caused by *Maize dwarf mosaic virus.*

FIG. 3.19. Leaf margin necrosis, caused by drought stress.

CHAPTER 4

Foliar and Aboveground Diseases

4.1 Anthracnose Leaf Blight

Fungus: *Colletotrichum graminicola*

Anthracnose leaf blight is caused by the same fungus that causes anthracnose stalk rot (section 6.1). However, anthracnose leaf blight  docs not necessarily lead to anthracnose stalk rot, and stalk rot can occur in the absence of leaf blight. Typically, anthracnose leaf blight is the first foliar disease to occur on corn during the growing season.

Symptoms and Signs

Symptoms appear first on the lowest leaves of the plant early in the season (Fig. 4.1). In the northern part of the U.S. Corn Belt and in Canada, symptoms may be found on upper leaves late in the season. Rapidly growing leaf tissue is less conducive to disease development, and symptoms on upper leaves are rare in most corn-producing regions.

Leaf lesions are oval or elongated, tan or brown with dark-brown or purple margins, and up to 1 inch (2.5 cm) long and ½ inch (1.0 cm) wide (Fig. 4.2). As the disease develops, the fungus produces fruiting structures (acervuli) on the dead leaf tissue: black, spiny structures (setae) visible with a 30× hand lens. On severely infected leaves, the lesions may grow together into large dead areas (Fig. 4.3); these leaves may turn yellow and wither. Plants with resistance to anthracnose leaf blight may have smaller, yellowish to brown lesions.

The early presence of leaf lesions does not necessarily correlate with the development of anthracnose stalk rot.

FIG. 4.2. Anthracnose leaf blight lesions.

FIG. 4.1. Symptoms of anthracnose leaf blight appear first on the lowest leaves.

FIG. 4.3. Anthracnose leaf blight lesions that have grown together.

Most Commonly Confused With

Eyespot (4.8) · Gray Leaf Spot (4.10) ·
Northern Corn Leaf Spot (4.18) · Southern Corn
Leaf Blight (4.21) · Nutrient Deficiency (8.1)

Anthracnose typically appears earlier in the season than eyespot and gray leaf spot. When symptoms are caused by a nutrient deficiency, fungal structures will not be present in the leaf lesions.

Favorable Conditions

The pathogen overwinters as mycelium in corn residue or seed. Spores are dispersed primarily by splashing water. Lesions on the lowest leaves are a source of inoculum for infection of the upper leaves. Disease development is favored by wet, cloudy conditions with moderately warm temperatures. Anthracnose is much more common in settings where corn follows corn or reduced tillage is practiced. Potassium-deficient leaves are often at greater risk for infection.

Management

Resistance. Resistant hybrids are available. However, resistance to anthracnose leaf blight and to anthracnose stalk rot are controlled by different genes, which may not be found in the same hybrid.

Cultural Practices. The inoculum level can be reduced by rotating crops or by reducing surface residue through tillage. If tillage is considered for decreasing pathogen levels, efforts should be made to minimize soil erosion and maintain soil quality. In reduced-tillage systems, resistance and rotation are important disease management practices.

Fungicides. Fungicides are available that have efficacy against anthracnose leaf blight. Decisions about foliar fungicide application should be based on a number of factors, including hybrid susceptibility to anthracnose leaf blight, amount of corn residue in the field, and potential for a positive economic return from application.

#Diagnostic Key Words

early season, wet, warm, fieldwide, lesions, lower canopy

4.2 Banded Leaf and Sheath Blight

Fungus: *Rhizoctonia solani* f. sp. *sasakii*

Banded leaf and sheath blight has been observed in the United States but is very rare. This disease has not been detected in Canada. It can be a serious problem in tropical and subtropical regions with hot and humid weather.

Symptoms and Signs

Lesions appear on leaf sheaths and leaves, displaying alternating gray or brownish discoloration and dark bands (Fig. 4.4). Other symptoms include ear rot, lodging, stalk lesions, and plant death.

Signs include sclerotia ranging from $\frac{1}{32}$ to $\frac{3}{16}$ inch (0.8 to 5.0 mm) in diameter, which frequently form behind leaf sheaths (Fig. 4.5). Fuzzy, light-brown mycelia can be observed on husks.

FIG. 4.4. Foliar symptoms of banded leaf and sheath blight.

Most Commonly Confused With

Stalk Rots (Chapter 6) • Diplodia Ear Rot (7.4) and other ear rots (Chapter 7) • Purple Leaf Sheath (8.3)

With other ear and stalk rots, sclerotia are not visible on husks and stalks. Because banded leaf and sheath blight is very rare in the United States, diagnosis should be confirmed using laboratory methods.

Favorable Conditions

Banded leaf and sheath blight is favored by hot and humid weather.

Management

Management of banded leaf and sheath blight is not warranted in the United States and Canada.

#Diagnostic Key Words

midseason, late season, wet, warm, death, signs, stalk lesions, lesions

FIG. 4.5. Formation of sclerotia behind the leaf sheath.

4.3 Common Rust

Fungus: *Puccinia sorghi*

Common rust can often be observed in fields throughout the United States and Canada. Even so, it is rarely of economic concern, except in seed corn, sweet corn, popcorn, and other specialty corn production.

Symptoms and Signs

Early symptoms of common rust are chlorotic flecks on the leaf surface. These flecks soon develop into powdery, brown to brick-red pustules that break through the leaf surface and produce spores (Fig. 4.6). Pustules are tiny (about ½-inch long [3 mm]) and oval or elongated, and they can be observed on upper and lower leaf surfaces in the middle to upper canopy (Fig. 4.7). Pustules may be surrounded by light-green to yellow halos, which can be seen when the leaf is backlit by sunlight. Leaf tissue may die, resulting in dead leaf lesions (Fig. 4.8). Entire leaves will die if the plant is severely infected. Pustules may also appear on husks, leaf sheaths, and stalks (Fig. 4.9).

FIG. 4.6. Pustules of common rust scattered across the leaf surface.

Most Commonly Confused With

Eyespot (4.8) • **Gray Leaf Spot (4.10)** •
Physoderma Brown Spot (4.19) • **Southern
Corn Leaf Blight (4.21)** • **Southern Rust (4.22)**

Common rust has brown to brick-red pustules on both the upper and lower leaf surfaces, whereas southern rust has orange to light-brown pustules on primarily the upper leaf surfaces. In addition, the pustules produced by common rust are generally less densely clustered than those produced by southern rust. The pustules of common rust also tend to be elongated, whereas those of southern rust are more oval to round. Mixed infections of both rust fungi can occur on the same plant, which can confuse diagnosis.

The presence of ruptured epidermal leaf tissue surrounding lesions can help distinguish common rust from gray leaf spot.

Favorable Conditions

The fungus that causes common rust generally requires living plant tissue to survive. Fungal spores that infect corn usually do not overwinter in northern areas. Every year, spores are blown north on wind currents from tropical areas and initiate new infections when they land on leaves.

The development of common rust is favored by high humidity with night temperatures of 65–70°F (18–21°C) and moderate daytime temperatures. Rust fungi require a short period of leaf wetness (as little as 6 hours) to cause infection. A single pustule on an infected leaf can contain more than 5,000 spores; therefore, secondary infections may cause disease to increase in intensity very quickly when weather conditions are favorable. Hot, dry weather limits disease development and stops pustules from producing the spores that infect corn, leaving small, dead areas of leaf tissue.

FIG. 4.7. Red, powdery, elongated pustules of common rust.

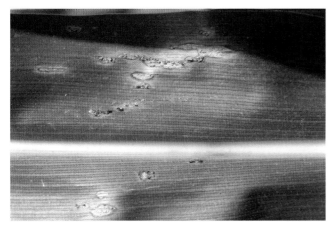

FIG. 4.8. Common rust pustules surrounded by dead leaf tissue.

FIG. 4.9. Common rust pustules on stalk tissue.

Management

Resistance. Resistance to common rust varies across corn hybrids. Most hybrids are fairly resistant, but some inbred lines are quite susceptible. All corn plants have age-related resistance to the rust fungi; mature leaves are less susceptible to infection.

Cultural Practices. Cultural practices do not influence the development of common rust, partially because the fungus does not survive in crop residue.

Fungicides. Fungicide applications may be needed for specialty corn and in environments conducive to disease development and spread.

#Diagnostic Key Words

midseason, late season, wet, cool, fieldwide, signs, stalk lesions, lesions, middle canopy, upper canopy

4.4 Common Smut

Fungus: *Ustilago maydis*

Common smut is found frequently throughout the United States and Canada, although it rarely causes economic concern.

Symptoms and Signs

Smut galls can form on corn stalks, leaves, ears, and tassels and can replace corn tissue from the early vegetative stages through maturity (Fig. 4.10). The galls are swollen, distorted, and covered with a glistening white to gray membrane. The membrane eventually ruptures to reveal a mass of dark-brown or black powdery spores (teliospores). On leaves, the galls usually do not rupture but harden to a white or green mass (Fig. 4.11). On stalks, the galls can cause yield loss through stunting or lodging (Fig. 4.12). Infections through the silks result in the replacement of kernels with smut galls. Infection is localized and will not spread throughout the plant. Thus, some ears may be free of symptoms, and galls can form on individual kernels.

FIG. 4.10. Common smut galls on an ear.

All aboveground plant parts can be affected by common smut (Fig. 4.13). Where galls form depends on the part of the plant that is actively growing at the time of infection.

Most Commonly Confused With

Head Smut (4.11)

Compared with the large, swollen galls produced by common smut, those produced by head smut have a thinner membrane. Head smut galls are also associated with abnormal vascular bundles on the ears or tassels.

Favorable Conditions

The fungus that causes common smut produces spores that overwinter in corn residue or soil. The fungus produces black teliospores that are resistant to environmental conditions, making them well suited for survival in the soil (Fig. 4.14). The teliospores germinate during the spring and summer and produce smaller spores (sporidia), which are spread by wind and water. Sporidia can infect plants through unwounded cells, but wounds caused by insects, detasseling, cultivation, hail, and blowing soil provide important infection sites.

FIG. 4.11. Common smut gall on a leaf.

FIG 4.13. Common smut galls may form in the tassels.

FIG. 4.12. Common smut gall on a stalk.

FIG. 4.14. Black teliospores in common smut galls.

Disease development is favored by excess nitrogen, excess manure application, herbicide injury, and relatively dry, warm weather.

Management

Management is not necessary for common smut. Hybrids vary in susceptibility, but most will not experience economic losses from this disease.

#Diagnostic Key Words

early season, midseason, late season, wounding, dry, warm, scattered, stunting, galls, lodging, signs

4.5 Corn Stunt

Spiroplasma: *Spiroplasma kunkelii*

Corn stunt is found mostly in the southern and eastern United States.

Symptoms and Signs

Symptoms include yellow spots that coalesce into stripes, along with stunting, shortened internodes (Fig. 4.15), proliferation of tillers, leaf reddening

FIG. 4.15. Shortened internodes caused by corn stunt.

FIG. 4.16. Leaf reddening caused by corn stunt.

(Fig. 4.16), formation of multiple and/or barren ears, and tassel sterility. Infected plants will generally die early, and their seed set will be poor.

Most Commonly Confused With

Maize Bushy Stunt (4.13) •
Maize Chlorotic Dwarf (4.14)

Laboratory diagnosis will be needed to distinguish among maize bushy stunt, maize chlorotic dwarf, and corn stunt.

Favorable Conditions

The corn stunt spiroplasma is transmitted by and overwinters in leafhoppers. Several other plant species are hosts of the pathogen. Continuous corn production favors disease.

Management

Management of corn stunt is very difficult. Planting hybrids with some level of resistance is the most effective approach, although breeding for resistance has been limited.

#Diagnostic Key Words

patchy, stunting, tillering, distortion, death, abnormal ears, leaf discoloration

4.6 Crazy Top

Oomycete: *Sclerophthora macrospora*

Crazy top is caused by a soilborne oomycete pathogen that infects corn throughout the United States and Canada, as well as other parts of the world.  This disease is generally not of economic concern.

Symptoms and Signs

Crazy top causes distortion and/or stunting of the corn plant and can appear from the early vegetative stages through maturity. Symptom expression varies widely. The tassel may proliferate, making the top of the plant look very bushy (which explains the name of this disease) (Fig. 4.17). The internodes

FIG. 4.17. A, Field view of corn plants with crazy top. **B,** Tassel distortion and proliferation of a single plant.

may be short or long (Fig. 4.18), and there may be a proliferation of ear shoots, leaves that are narrow and straplike, excessive tillering (Fig. 4.19), and a complete lack of ear and tassel formation. Pollen is not produced, stunting may occur, and leaves may display yellow stripes.

FIG. 4.18. Shortened internodes caused by crazy top.

FIG. 4.19. Excessive tillering and stunting—both characteristics of crazy top.

Most Commonly Confused With

Sorghum Downy Mildew (4.20) • Herbicide Injury (8.2)

Distortion of plant tissue and tassel proliferation on plants distinguishes crazy top from other disorders and diseases (Fig. 4.20).

Favorable Conditions

The pathogen overwinters as oospores within infected tissue or in the soil. During periods of flooding, the oospores germinate and swimming spores (zoospores) are produced. The zoospores infect the growing points of young corn plants, which are very susceptible. Thus, prolonged flooding (24–48 hours), ponding, and intense rain during early vegetative stages can all lead to infection.

Wild grasses, sorghum, and small grains are also attacked by this pathogen. Therefore, inoculum can remain present in the field for many years when corn is not grown.

Management

Management of this disease is rarely warranted, but when it is, cultural practices should be implemented.

Cultural Practices. Providing proper soil drainage will reduce the risk of infection and

FIG. 4.20. Distortion and proliferation of the tassel.

subsequent infection. In seed and specialty corn production, physically removing (roguing) infected plants from the field may reduce inoculum levels.

Weed Management. Managing grassy weeds will reduce inoculum sources.

Diagnostic Key Words

midseason, wet, ponding/wet soils, scattered, stunting, tillering, distortion, abnormal ears, leaf discoloration

4.7 Diplodia Leaf Streak

Fungus: *Stenocarpella macrospora*

Diplodia leaf streak is caused by a different fungus than the one that causes Diplodia stalk rot (section 6.4) and Diplodia ear rot (*Stenocarpella maydis*) (section 7.4); however, the leaf streak fungus may also cause ear rot. Diplodia leaf streak has been reported sporadically in the United States.

Symptoms and Signs

Symptoms may occur on all leaves, including the ear leaves. The initial symptom is the appearance of small, elliptical, light- to dark-colored lesions (Fig. 4.21). These spots expand into long, narrow streaks (Fig. 4.22), which can be nearly as long as the entire leaf and up to about 1½ inches wide (38 mm) (Fig. 4.23). Small fungal structures (less than ⅛ inch in diameter [3mm]) that appear as black spots (pycnidia) may be observed within the leaf streaks (Fig. 4.24).

The fungus that causes this disease can infect any plant tissue at any growth stage.

FIG. 4.21. Early lesion of Diplodia leaf streak.

FIG. 4.22. Streaklike lesions of Diplodia leaf streak.

FIG. 4.23. Developed lesions of Diplodia leaf streak.

FIG. 4.24. Pycnidia within Diplodia leaf streak lesions.

Most Commonly Confused With

Goss's Wilt (4.9) • **Northern Corn Leaf Blight (4.17)** • **Stewart's Disease (4.23)**

No bacterial exudate is observed with Diplodia leaf streak, and obvious pycnidia only occur in lesions of Diplodia leaf streak.

Favorable Conditions

The fungus survives on residue and seed and may be more prevalent in fields with infested corn residue. Average temperatures and moderate humidity levels favor disease development. Secondary infections can occur when lesions produce spores, creating inoculum that infects other plants or plant parts.

Management

Because of the sporadic occurrence of Diplodia leaf streak in the United States, research aimed at managing it has been limited.

Cultural Practices. Inoculum can be reduced by rotating crops or by reducing surface residue through tillage. If tillage is considered to decrease pathogen levels, efforts should be made to minimize soil erosion and maintain soil quality. In reduced-tillage systems, resistance and rotation are very important disease management practices.

Fungicides. Current fungicide labels do not list Diplodia leaf streak as a targeted disease.

#Diagnostic Key Words

midseason, late season, wet, warm, lesions, signs, patchy

4.8 Eyespot

Fungus: *Aureobasidium zeae*

Eyespot is prevalent in the northern part of the U.S. Corn Belt and in Canada during cool years, but it rarely results in yield losses for commercial hybrids.

Symptoms and Signs

Eyespot may appear early in the season on the lower leaves and again near the end of the season on the upper leaves. Initially, the lesions are ⅛–¼ inch (3–6 mm) in diameter and appear as water-soaked or chlorotic, circular spots; they often develop in clusters (Fig. 4.25). The tissue at the center of each spot later dies and turns tan with a brown or purple ring at the margins. Each spot is also surrounded by a yellow halo, which can be seen clearly when the leaf is backlit (Fig. 4.26). Spots may join to form large necrotic areas (Fig. 4.27), and the entire leaf may die. The spots remain visible even after the leaf dies.

FIG. 4.25. Cluster of eyespot lesions.

Most Commonly Confused With

Anthracnose Leaf Blight (4.1) • Common Rust (4.3) • Gray Leaf Spot (4.10) • Holcus Leaf Spot (4.12) • Physoderma Brown Spot (4.19) • Southern Rust (4.22) • Lesion Mimic (8.3) • Insect Injury (8.4)

Physoderma brown spot produces brown splotches on the midrib, which does not occur with eyespot. Orange spores that can be easily wiped off the surfaces of lesions with the forefinger will be present with southern rust.

Favorable Conditions

The fungus that causes eyespot overwinters in corn residue, and in wet conditions, it produces spores that are spread by splashing water and wind.

FIG. 4.26. Backlit eyespot lesions surrounded by halos.

FIG. 4.27. Coalesced eyespot lesions.

Eyespot occurs much more commonly when corn follows corn with reduced tillage, and it is favored by cool temperatures (70°F [21°C]) and rainy conditions or persistent dew.

Management

Resistance. Resistant hybrids are available.

Cultural Practices. Inoculum levels can be reduced by rotating crops and reducing surface residue through tillage. If tillage is considered to decrease pathogen levels, efforts should be made to minimize soil erosion and maintain soil quality. In reduced-tillage systems, resistance and rotation are very important disease management practices.

Fungicides. Fungicides are currently labeled for use and can be effective against eyespot. However, efficacy may vary based on disease progression, environmental conditions before and after application, spray coverage, active ingredient, and other factors.

#Diagnostic Key Words

midseason, late season, wet, cool, fieldwide, death, lesions, lower canopy, upper canopy

4.9 Goss's Wilt

Bacterium: *Clavibacter michiganensis* subsp. *nebraskensis*

The disease commonly referred to as Goss's wilt has both a wilt phase and a leaf blight phase; however, the two phases are not always linked. Goss's wilt can cause substantial yield losses under favorable conditions. It has been reported in many midwestern and southern states in the United States and in some Canadian provinces.

Symptoms and Signs

Goss's wilt has two phases: (1) the wilt phase is caused by a systemic infection, and (2) the leaf blight phase is characterized by foliar lesions that typically develop first in the middle to upper canopy (Fig. 4.28). The wilt phase of the disease can transition into the leaf blight phase. Corn can be infected at any stage of growth, although the wilt phase is often first observed when infection occurs before V6.

The leaf blight phase is the most common. It produces lesions that are long, grayish-green to black, and water soaked and that have wavy margins. The development of dark-green or black flecks (resembling freckles) within lesions is a distinctive symptom of this disease (Fig. 4.29). These water-soaked flecks are transparent when the leaf is backlit

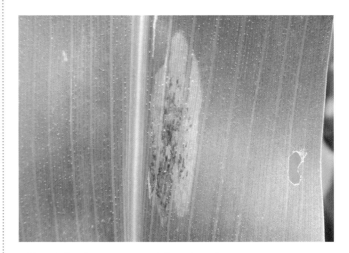

FIG. 4.28. Early lesion of Goss's wilt.

by being held up to the sun (Fig. 4.30); therefore, they can be distinguished from saprophytic fungi (dark spots), which may be visible in the dead tissue of the lesion. Droplets of bacterial exudate, which resembles maple syrup, may eventually ooze from the lesions. When the droplets dry, they leave shiny deposits on the leaf surface (Fig. 4.31). On a susceptible hybrid, the lesions coalesce to cover a substantial portion of the leaf. As the lesions age, they gradually lose the gray-green color and fade to tan, which makes them easily confused with the lesions caused by other diseases and disorders. Bacterial streaming can be observed when the cut section of the edge of a lesion is placed in water and viewed with a microscope.

In the wilt phase of the disease, systemically infected plants may have orange or brown discoloration of the vascular tissue (Fig. 4.32),

FIG. 4.31. Shiny bacterial exudate associated with Goss's wilt lesions.

FIG. 4.32. Discoloration in the pith of a plant affected by Goss's wilt.

FIG. 4.29. Long lesions and dark "freckles" are characteristic symptoms of Goss's wilt.

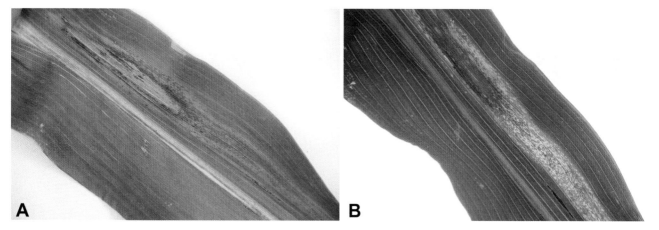

A **B**

FIG. 4.30. Water-soaked flecks symptomatic of Goss's wilt are transparent when the leaf is backlit. **A,** Leaf under normal lighting. **B,** Leaf held up to the sun.

and plants may wilt as if drought stressed. These plants may also have deteriorated pith, and they may lodge or break easily. These systemically infected plants may stand out among the surrounding green plants.

Most Commonly Confused With

Diplodia Leaf Streak (4.7) · Northern Corn Leaf Blight (4.17) · Stewart's Disease (4.23) · Nitrogen or Potassium Deficiency (8.1) · Drought (8.3) · High Temperatures (8.3) · Insect Injury (8.4)

The freckling and shiny bacterial ooze associated with lesions of Goss's wilt help distinguish it from other diseases and disorders. However, diagnosing this disease in the field may be difficult based on symptom appearance. Laboratory analysis is often necessary to confirm this disease.

Favorable Conditions

The causal bacteria overwinter primarily in infested corn residue, and they are spread by splashing water, wind, and leaf-to-leaf contact. The bacteria enter the plant primarily through wounds caused by hail, blowing soil, or wind but can also enter through the stomata or leaf edges. Thus, severe weather events increase the disease risk.

Although seed can be infected, seed-to-seedling transmission is very low, occurring in less than 1% of infected seed. Infested seed is important, however, as it may introduce the disease into new areas. Transportation of infested residue can also be a significant method of introducing the bacteria into new areas. Some grass weeds are hosts for the bacteria and can serve as reservoirs from which the bacteria spread to corn.

Hot, dry weather slow disease development, making symptoms of Goss's wilt harder to distinguish from those of other disorders, such as drought stress. Warm (80°F [27°C]), wet weather favors rapid development of disease.

Management

Resistance. Hybrids react to Goss's wilt in various ways; some are highly susceptible and others highly resistant. The resistance of a particular hybrid should be determined prior to planting.

Cultural Practices. Rotating crops and reducing surface residue through tillage can decrease the levels of inoculum in a field. If tillage is considered to decrease pathogen levels, efforts should be made to minimize soil erosion and maintain soil quality.

Fungicides. Foliar-applied fungicides are not effective against this disease. Field trials evaluating copper products, inorganic acids, and other bactericides have indicated that applying these chemicals is not economically feasible given the limited efficacy of these products and the likelihood that multiple applications will be needed throughout the season.

Weed Management. Good weed management can reduce species of grass weed that serve as sources of the disease.

#Diagnostic Key Words

early season, midseason, late season, wilting, wounding, wet, warm, fieldwide (blight), scattered (wilt), lodging, rotting stalk interior, lesions (blight), middle canopy, upper canopy, leaf margins dead

4.10 Gray Leaf Spot

Fungus: *Cercospora zeae-maydis*

Gray leaf spot occurs every year in the United States and in Ontario, Canada, and it may cause economic losses under conditions that are favorable for disease development. This disease is especially problematic in the eastern United States and in southern Ontario, and it has become more important in the western U.S. Corn Belt.

Symptoms and Signs

In hybrid corn, symptoms first appear on the lower leaves about 2–3 weeks before tasseling. Lesions may appear earlier when conditions are highly favorable for disease development and in seed production fields. Leaf lesions begin as small, round or jagged, light-tan spots (Fig. 4.33) and expand to become long (up to 2 inches [50 mm]), narrow, and rectangular (Fig. 4.34). The lesions are usually confined by and expand parallel to the leaf veins, and later, the lesions may turn gray. Depending on the corn hybrid, the lesions may be surrounded by yellow to orange halos.

The development of lesions progresses into the middle to upper canopy, based on weather conditions. Large, rectangular lesions are often visible in the lower canopy (Fig. 4.35), while younger, smaller lesions may appear in the upper canopy. Lesions can coalesce and blight large areas of leaves (Fig. 4.36).

Yield loss depends on the number of lesions and how far up the canopy they occur as plants enter tasseling and pollination. If lesions reach the ear leaves or higher during the 2 weeks before and after tasseling, yield loss may occur, particularly if the hybrid is susceptible.

FIG. 4.34. Elongated lesions that expand parallel to leaf veins, characteristic of gray leaf spot.

FIG. 4.35. Gray leaf spot lesions in the lower canopy.

FIG. 4.33. Early lesions of gray leaf spot.

FIG. 4.36. Lesions join and form blighted areas of leaf tissue.

FIG. 4.37. Gray leaf spot lesions on the husk.

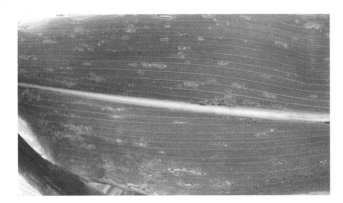

FIG. 4.38. Small gray leaf spot lesions on a hybrid with moderate resistance to the disease.

On susceptible hybrids, lesions may also appear on the leaf sheaths and husks (Fig. 4.37). Hybrids with partial resistance to gray leaf spot may not experience the characteristic lesion expansion. These hybrids restrict lesion growth, so the lesions may remain small (Fig. 4.38).

Most Commonly Confused With

Anthracnose Leaf Blight (4.1) • Common Rust (4.3) • Eyespot (4.8) • Northern Corn Leaf Spot (race 3) (4.18) • Southern Corn Leaf Blight (4.21) • Nutrient Deficiency (8.1) • Insect Injury (8.4)

Gray leaf spot lesions are restricted by the leaf veins and begin in the lower canopy. Early lesions and lesions that form on a hybrid resistant to gray leaf spot may resemble lesions associated with race 3 of northern corn leaf spot. For these types of lesions, laboratory diagnosis may be needed to confirm the disease by examining fungal spores of the causal organism.

Favorable Conditions

Gray leaf spot is more severe when corn follows corn in the same field and in reduced and no-till systems. The fungus survives in corn residue, and spores are dispersed by wind and splashing water.

Warm temperatures and relative humidity greater than 90% favor disease development. Symptoms are commonly observed following long periods of heavy dew and overcast days and in bottomlands and fields adjacent to woods, where humidity is usually high and dew persists well into the morning. The fungus can infect plants during a period of high humidity, but symptoms may not appear for 2–3 weeks in some cases. Given this long latent period, symptoms may seem to appear suddenly, but in fact, infection occurs several weeks before symptoms of the disease are observed. Hot, dry weather will restrict disease development and spread.

Hybrid susceptibility and weather conditions strongly influence disease development; thus, gray leaf spot can be locally severe but not cause widespread damage throughout a region. In late-planted corn, the initial infection occurs at earlier growth stages, which can result in higher levels of infection and increased yield loss.

Management

Resistance. Some hybrids are more resistant to gray leaf spot than others. Hybrids with adequate resistance should be planted in fields where the disease commonly occurs—for example, fields near river bottoms.

Cultural Practices. Inoculum levels can be reduced by rotating crops and reducing surface residue through tillage. If tillage is considered to decrease pathogen levels, efforts should be made to minimize soil erosion and maintain soil quality. In reduced-tillage systems, resistance and rotation are very important disease management practices.

Fungicides. Fungicides are currently labeled for use against gray leaf spot. However, efficacy may vary based on disease progression, environmental conditions before and after application, spray coverage, active ingredient, and other factors.

#Diagnostic Key Words

midseason, late season, wet, warm, fieldwide, death, lesions, lower canopy

4.11 Head Smut

Fungus: *Sphacelotheca reiliana*

Head smut occurs in isolated areas throughout the United States and Canada.

Symptoms and Signs

Although infection occurs in seedlings, symptoms of head smut are first noticed when the ears and tassels emerge. Often, the entire ear shoot becomes a large gall covered only by husk leaves (Fig. 4.39). Galls form on tassels but rarely on leaves. The gall is initially covered with a thin layer of tissue, which breaks open to expose the black spore masses and threadlike remains of the vascular bundles (Fig. 4.40).

FIG. 4.39. Head smut ear gall wrapped in the husk.

FIG. 4.40. Black spore masses in place of an ear, characteristic of head smut.

Leaflike structures develop on the tassels and ears.

The ears may be aborted and replaced with an abundance of leafy tissue. Plants may also be severely stunted or have an excessive number of tillers (Fig. 4.41). When present on leaves, galls occur in long, narrow strips.

Most Commonly Confused With

Common Smut (4.4)

Common smut galls do not exhibit vascular bundles, which are typical of head smut galls. Common smut galls also have a more robust outer covering.

Favorable Conditions

The fungus that causes head smut survives in soil as long-lived spores (teliospores), and the germinating spores infect young seedlings. The fungus grows systemically within the developing plant without expressing symptoms and eventually moves into the ear and tassel (Fig. 4.42).

Low levels of soil moisture and temperatures between 70 and 82°F (21 and 28°C) provide optimum conditions for infection. Head smut occurs most commonly in soils with nitrogen deficiencies.

Teliospores may be seedborne, but seed is not considered an important source of inoculum.

Management

Management of head smut is usually not necessary. In high-risk fields, the following practices can be implemented.

Cultural Practices. Spores are long lived in soil, which reduces the usefulness of crop rotation. Rotation will reduce the buildup of inoculum; however, some strains of the fungus can infect both corn and sorghum. Maintaining an adequate nitrogen level during the early growth stages reduces susceptibility. Planting early or using a fast-emerging hybrid may allow seedlings to escape infection.

Fungicides. Systemic seed treatments are available that have efficacy against head smut. Most commercial corn seed is treated with a fungicide.

#Diagnostic Key Words

midseason, late season, dry, warm, scattered, stunting, tillering, galls, distortion, signs

FIG. 4.41. Stunted plant affected by head smut.

FIG. 4.42. Head smut gall on a tassel.

4.12 Holcus Leaf Spot

Bacterium: *Pseudomonas syringae* pv. *syringae*

The bacterium that causes holcus leaf spot has a wide host range and is found across the United States and Canada. It usually does not cause major losses to corn.

Symptoms and Signs

Leaf lesions appear before the R1 growth stage and are found from the center of the leaf to the tip (Fig. 4.43). They are initially dark green and oval to irregular in shape, and they have water soaking at the margins (Fig. 4.44). Depending on the hybrid, a light-brown border may appear around the lesion. A single lesion is initially about ¼ inch (6 mm) in diameter, but lesions may enlarge and grow together into irregular spots and streaks of dead tissue (Fig. 4.45). Later, the lesions dry out and turn light tan, and they usually do not have borders. The dry lesions have a papery texture. Lesions do not develop across the midrib of the leaf, and the ooze that accompanies bacterial diseases of corn is sometimes seen in the centers of leaf lesions.

Holcus leaf spot often appears several days after a heavy rain, but after the initial infection, it does not spread to new leaves.

Most Commonly Confused With

Eyespot (4.8) • Herbicide Injury (drift or application injury caused by paraquat) (8.2)) • Lesion Mimic (8.3)

Holcus leaf spot typically appears earlier in the season than eyespot. Symptom patterns should be checked to rule out herbicide injury.

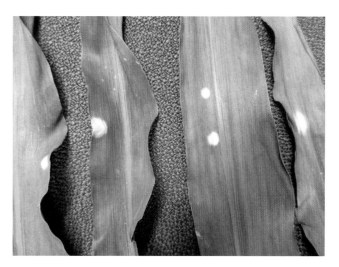

FIG. 4.44. Water-soaked margins of holcus leaf spot lesions.

FIG. 4.43. Lesions near the leaf tip, symptomatic of holcus leaf spot.

FIG. 4.45. Holcus leaf spot lesions grow together and blight the leaf.

Favorable Conditions

The bacterium that causes holcus leaf spot overwinters in crop residue and on grass species, including weeds. Bacteria are splashed onto leaves and invade plants through the stomata and wounds caused by hail, blowing soil, and wind.

Holcus leaf spot often develops following warm, rainy weather early in the season.

Management

Management of holcus leaf spot is rarely warranted. Although the disease may cause concern based on symptom appearance, no in-season treatment is available.

#Diagnostic Key Words

early season, midseason, late season, wounding, wet, warm, fieldwide, lesions

4.13 Maize Bushy Stunt

Phytoplasma: 'Candidatus Phytoplasma asteris'

Maize bushy stunt occurs on corn in the southern United States.

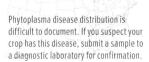

Phytoplasma disease distribution is difficult to document. If you suspect your crop has this disease, submit a sample to a diagnostic laboratory for confirmation.

Symptoms and Signs

Symptoms of maize bushy stunt include leaf yellowing at the margins of whorls; older leaves have reddish tips (Fig. 4.46). New leaves developing from the whorls are short, torn, and twisted, and they display varying amounts of yellowing and reddening. A distinguishing symptom of this disease is a bushy plant caused by the proliferation of tillers. The development of multiple small ears and poor root systems, as well as stunting and plant death, may also occur.

Most Commonly Confused With

Corn Stunt (4.5) • Maize Chlorotic Dwarf (4.14) • Maize Chlorotic Mottle (4.15) • Maize Dwarf Mosaic (4.16)

Laboratory diagnosis will be needed to distinguish maize bushy stunt from these diseases.

FIG. 4.46. Yellow and red leaf discoloration, characteristic of maize bushy stunt.

Favorable Conditions

The maize bushy stunt phytoplasma is transmitted by and overwinters in leafhoppers. The only other plant host for this pathogen is teosinte, an ancestor of corn.

Continuous planting of corn favors development of this disease.

Management

Resistance. Management of maize bushy stunt is very difficult. Planting hybrids with some level of resistance is the most likely means of control, although breeding for resistance has been limited.

Diagnostic Key Words

patchy, stunting, tillering, distortion, death, leaf discoloration

4.14 Maize Chlorotic Dwarf

Virus: *Maize chlorotic dwarf virus* (*Waikavirus*)

Maize chlorotic dwarf virus (MCDV) occurs in the southern United States, from the Atlantic Coast to Texas.

Virus disease distribution is difficult to document. If you suspect your crop has this disease, submit a sample to a diagnostic laboratory for confirmation.

Symptoms and Signs

Symptom expression of maize chlorotic dwarf varies according to corn genetics, time of infection, viral strain, and environment. The most characteristic symptom is chlorosis of the secondary leaf veins, which produces fine stripes; these stripes are most visible on the undersides of leaves (Fig. 4.47). The leaf veins are swollen and appear dull and rough (Fig. 4.48). Other symptoms include

FIG. 4.47. Chlorosis of the secondary leaf veins caused by maize chlorotic dwarf.

FIG. 4.48. Chlorosis of leaf veins caused by maize chlorotic dwarf.

chlorosis of the leaves or the plant in general, along with reddening of leaves, shortened upper internodes (resulting in plant stunting), and torn, distorted leaves.

MCDV and *Maize dwarf mosaic virus* (MDMV; section 4.16) often infect a plant simultaneously.

Most Commonly Confused With

Corn Stunt (4.5) • Maize Bushy Stunt (4.13) • Maize Chlorotic Mottle (4.15) • Maize Dwarf Mosaic (4.16) • Nutrient Deficiency (8.1) • Herbicide Injury (8.2) • Lesion Mimic (8.3) • Insect Injury (8.4)

Laboratory diagnosis will be needed to distinguish maize chlorotic dwarf from other virus diseases and nutrient deficiencies.

Favorable Conditions

The virus that causes maize chlorotic dwarf overwinters in johnsongrass, sorghum, and other grasses, and the primary vector is a single species of leafhopper. Disease development is favored by leafhoppers thriving and by proximity to johnsongrass.

Management

Resistance. Hybrids with resistance or tolerance to MCDV are available.

Weed Management. Weed management will reduce the spread of maize chlorotic dwarf from johnsongrass. The incidence of MCDV has been drastically reduced by the elimination of grassy weeds within cornfields following the adoption of herbicide-resistant hybrids.

#Diagnostic Key Words

patchy, stunting, distortion, leaf discoloration

4.15 Maize Chlorotic Mottle

Virus: *Maize chlorotic mottle virus* (*Sobemovirus*)

Maize chlorotic mottle is caused by *Maize chlorotic mottle virus* (MCMV). MCMV has been reported in a few corn-growing states in the U.S. West and in Hawaii.

Virus disease distribution is difficult to document. If you suspect your crop has this disease, submit a sample to a diagnostic laboratory for confirmation.

Symptoms and Signs

Symptoms of maize chlorotic mottle vary and include development of a leaf mosaic, which appears as thin, yellowish streaks running along leaf veins (Fig. 4.49); the mosaic turns into mottling followed by leaf and plant death (Figs. 4.50 and 4.51). Additional symptoms are shortened internodes, which causes stunting (Fig. 4.52), as well as poorly filled and deformed ears, husks with early senescence, and tassel stunting.

Premature plant aging can occur when corn is simultaneously infected by MCMV and another virus, such as *Maize mosaic virus* (MMV). Infection by MCMV and one of three potyviruses—*Maize dwarf mosaic virus* (MDMV), *Sugarcane mosaic virus* (SCMV), or *Wheat streak mosaic virus* (WSMV)—can result in corn lethal necrosis.

FIG. 4.49. Thin, yellow streaks, early symptoms of maize chlorotic mottle.

Most Commonly Confused With

Maize Bushy Stunt (4.13) • Maize Chlorotic Dwarf (4.14) • Maize Dwarf Mosaic (4.16) • Other Viruses (4.24) • Nutrient Deficiency (8.1) • Herbicide Injury (8.2) • Lesion Mimic (8.3) • Insect Injury (8.4)

Laboratory diagnosis will be needed to distinguish maize chlorotic mottle from other virus diseases and nutrient deficiencies.

FIG. 4.50. Mottling caused by maize chlorotic mottle.

Favorable Conditions

MCMV is spread by a number of vectors, including the corn flea beetle, the corn thrips, and the northern, western, and southern corn rootworms. It can also be spread mechanically and with seed.

Disease development is favored by continuous production of corn in the same field.

Management

Cultural Practices. Effective practices include reducing mechanical traffic in the field and eliminating infected plants.

Insect Management. Managing insect vectors may reduce the incidence of disease. However, the traditional use of insecticides has been only moderately effective against nonpersistently transmitted viruses, such as MCMV.

Weed Management. Effective weed management will help to reduce disease.

#Diagnostic Key Words

patchy, stunting, distortion, death, abnormal ears, leaf discoloration

FIG. 4.51. Leaf death caused by maize chlorotic mottle.

FIG. 4.52. Stunting caused by maize chlorotic mottle.

4.16 Maize Dwarf Mosaic

Virus: *Maize dwarf mosaic virus* (*Potyvirus*)

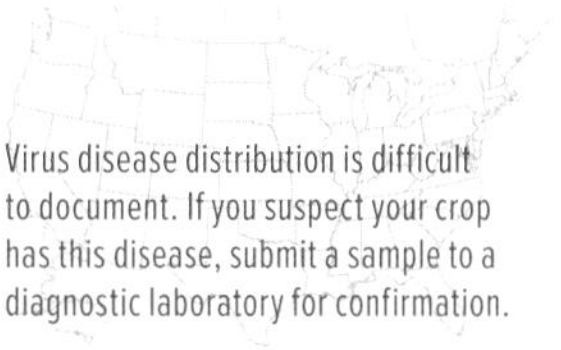

Maize dwarf mosaic is caused by several strains of *Maize dwarf mosaic virus* (MDMV), some of which have been reclassified as *Sugarcane mosaic virus* (SCMV). Both viruses infect cornfields across the United States and Canada.

Virus disease distribution is difficult to document. If you suspect your crop has this disease, submit a sample to a diagnostic laboratory for confirmation.

Symptoms and Signs

Symptom expression varies according to corn genetics, MDMV strain, and time of infection. Initially, plants develop a stippled mottle or mosaic of light and dark green, which may turn into narrow streaks on the youngest leaves (Figs. 4.53 and 4.54). Shortening of internodes may also occur, causing plants to have a stunted, bunchy appearance (Fig. 4.55), along with profuse tillering. Red streaks may appear on older leaves. As plants mature and temperatures rise, the mosaic symptoms often disappear and young leaves become increasingly yellow. Infected plants may be barren or have small ears and aborted kernels. Symptoms are most severe on young plants that become infected in the seedling stage; plants infected at pollination or later may appear normal.

MDMV-infected plants are predisposed to root rot. MDMV infection can also increase the severity of foliar disease.

Most Commonly Confused With

Maize Bushy Stunt (4.13) • Maize Chlorotic Dwarf (4.14) • Maize Chlorotic Mottle (4.15) • Other Viruses (4.24) • Nutrient Deficiency (8.1) • Herbicide Injury (8.2) • Lesion Mimic (8.3) • Insect Injury (8.4)

Laboratory diagnosis will be needed to distinguish maize dwarf mosaic from other virus diseases, physiological disorders, and nutrient deficiencies.

FIG. 4.54. Heavy mosaic symptoms on the youngest leaves, characteristic of maize dwarf mosaic.

FIG. 4.53. Mosaic streaks caused by maize dwarf mosaic.

FIG. 4.55. Shortened internodes and mosaic caused by maize dwarf mosaic.

Favorable Conditions

MDMV overwinters primarily in johnsongrass, and it is transmitted to corn by several species of aphid. However, many wild and cultivated grasses are also hosts, including sorghum. The johnsongrass-infecting strains of MDMV occur primarily where johnsongrass grows, but aphids carrying MDMV are commonly carried northward on wind currents. Virus particles can be carried for up to 6 hours on the mouthparts of aphids.

Disease development is favored by average to warm temperatures and proximity to johnsongrass.

Management

Resistance. Resistant hybrids are available.

Cultural Practices. Incidence of the virus is greatly reduced in early planted corn, because aphid populations do not build up until plants are past the highly susceptible seedling stage.

Weed Management. Weed management will reduce spread of the virus from grasses. Managing johnsongrass with the modern herbicides used in corn-to-soybean rotations has greatly reduced the incidence of MDMV.

#Diagnostic Key Words

patchy, warm, stunting, tillering, abnormal ears, leaf discoloration

4.17 Northern Corn Leaf Blight

Fungus: *Setosphaeria turcica* (synonym: *Exserohilum turcicum*)

Northern corn leaf blight (NCLB) is one of the most consistently damaging foliar diseases of field corn in the northern U.S. Corn Belt and in Canada. Thirteen races of the causal fungus have been identified worldwide, and at least four races exist in North America.

Symptoms and Signs

Leaf lesions are from 1 to 6-plus inches (2.5–15.0 cm) in length and run parallel to leaf margins. These long, elliptical (cigar-shaped) lesions are gray-green at first but then turn pale gray or tan (Figs. 4.56 and 4.57). The margins of young lesions often have a silvery, water-soaked appearance (Fig. 4.58). Lesion development is not restricted by leaf veins. Under moist conditions, lesions produce dark-gray spores, such that the centers of lesions have a dirty, grayish appearance (Fig. 4.59).

Symptoms of NCLB become visible on leaves prior to tasseling. Symptoms usually appear on the lower

FIG. 4.56. Classic cigar-shaped lesion of northern corn leaf blight.

leaves first and progress upward to the higher leaves if favorable conditions continue. Rain and wind dispersal of spores can cause symptoms to occur in the upper canopy first. Infection often takes place within the whorl, which may cause multiple lesions to form in bands across leaves. Lesions may continue to develop in size and coalesce, causing leaves to die prematurely (Fig. 4.60).

Lesions may also form on leaf sheaths and the outer husks of ears, but the kernels are not infected. Symptoms may vary in appearance depending on hybrid resistance.

Most Commonly Confused With

Diplodia Leaf Streak (4.7) • Goss's Wilt (4.9) • Northern Corn Leaf Spot (4.18) • Stewart's Disease (4.23) • High Temperatures (8.3) • Insect Injury (8.4)

The lesions caused by northern corn leaf blight are more elliptical than those caused by many other foliar diseases of corn. Laboratory diagnosis may be needed to distinguish symptoms on some hybrids.

FIG. 4.59. Dirty, grayish appearance of a lesion produced by spores of the fungus that causes northern corn leaf blight.

FIG. 4.57. Multiple elliptical lesions of northern corn leaf blight.

FIG. 4.58. Early lesions of northern corn leaf blight.

FIG. 4.60. Northern corn leaf blight lesions can grow and coalesce, blighting the leaf tissue.

Favorable Conditions

The fungus that causes NCLB overwinters as mycelium and spores in corn residue, and spores are dispersed by wind and splashing water. Disease development is favored by extended periods of leaf wetness (rain or dew) and by moderate temperatures (64–81°F [17–27°C]). An early infection that spreads from the lower canopy to the upper canopy can be very damaging.

Management

Resistance. Several types of resistance are available to control NCLB. Different resistance genes (*Ht* genes) may be used, but some races of the causal fungus can cause susceptible reactions on hybrids with specific *Ht* genes. *Ht* genes do not provide immunity against infection, but they may make lesions appear differently than they would on a susceptible hybrid. For instance, some *Ht* genes reduce lesion size by about 50% and produce lesions with chlorotic borders (Fig. 4.61). In such a case, races of the fungus that are controlled by the *Ht* gene will produce light-green to yellow lesions, instead of tan to brown lesions (dead tissue). Other *Ht* genes may slow disease development by restricting the sizes of lesions caused by affected races of the fungus. Another type of resistance (polygenic resistance) confers resistance to all races and results in reduced sporulation of the fungus and reduced lesion size and number.

Cultural Practices. Inoculum levels can be reduced by rotating crops and reducing surface residue through tillage. If tillage is considered to decrease pathogen levels, efforts should be made to minimize soil erosion and maintain soil quality. In reduced-tillage systems, resistance and rotation are very important disease management practices.

Fungicides. Fungicides are registered for use on NCLB and may be necessary to manage the disease in certain situations. When scouting and weather forecasts indicate that the potential for disease development is high, applying fungicides at the tasseling to early silking stages (VT–R1) has the greatest likelihood of economic return. It is important to protect the ear leaf and the leaves above it as the plant enters the reproductive stages.

#Diagnostic Key Words

midseason, late season, wet, fieldwide, death, lesions, lower canopy

FIG. 4.61. Lesions produced on a hybrid with *Ht* genes are restricted in size.

Northern Corn Leaf Spot

Fungus: *Bipolaris zeicola*
(synonym: *Cochliobolus carbonum***)**

Northern corn leaf spot (NCLS) is also known as Carbonum leaf spot and was previously called Helminthosporium leaf spot. There are five known races of the fungus that causes this disease, and unlike other fungal races, these races are differentiated by symptom variations on corn. Northern corn leaf spot is considered relatively unimportant in the United States and Canada, except on the susceptible inbred lines used in seed corn production.

Symptoms and Signs

The symptoms of NCLS vary depending on the fungus race and corn genetics (Fig. 4.62). Race 0 is relatively unimportant.

Race 1 produces circular or oval foliar lesions that are approximately ½ inch (13 mm) wide and 1 inch (25 mm) long. These lesions generally have concentric zones. Infected kernels can develop a black, feltlike mold (Fig. 4.63).

Race 2 produces oblong, blocky, brown spots on leaves that are ¼–½ inch (6.5–13.0 mm) wide and 1 inch (25.0 mm) long. A black, feltlike mold can be produced on infected kernels, as occurs with race 1.

Race 3 causes the development of long, narrow lesions up to 1 inch long. The lesions are light tan and surrounded by darker borders, and they form in a series or string (sometimes called a string of pearls) (Fig. 4.64). These lesions occur most commonly on the leaves, sheaths, and husks.

Race 4 also produces long, narrow, blocky lesions (similar to those produced by race 2), but the lesions may have concentric zones within them. Infected leaves may have a reddish-brown appearance.

Severe infection by any race can kill entire leaves. The disease appears more often in the lower canopy.

Most Commonly Confused With

Anthracnose Leaf Blight (4.1) · Gray Leaf Spot (4.10) · Northern Corn Leaf Blight (4.17) · Southern Corn Leaf Blight (4.21) · Nigrospora Ear Rot (7.7)

Laboratory diagnosis is recommended to distinguish northern corn leaf spot from other foliar diseases and to differentiate the races of northern corn leaf spot.

FIG. 4.62. Lesions of northern corn leaf spot (race unknown).

FIG. 4.63. Ear mold caused by race 1 of the northern corn leaf spot fungus.

Favorable Conditions

The causal fungus overwinters as mycelium and spores in corn residue, and the spores are dispersed by wind and splashing water. Thus, northern corn leaf spot may be more prevalent in fields with infested corn residue and when unusually high rainfall occurs during the late summer.

For race 2, disease development is favored by warm, humid weather, whereas for race 3, disease development is favored by cool, humid weather.

Management

Disease management is rarely warranted for northern corn leaf spot. When management is needed, the following options should be considered.

Resistance. Resistant hybrids and inbred lines are available.

Cultural Practices. Inoculum levels can be reduced by rotating crops and reducing surface residue through tillage. If tillage is considered to decrease pathogen levels, efforts should be made to minimize soil erosion and maintain soil quality. In reduced-tillage systems, resistance and rotation are very important disease management practices.

Fungicides. Fungicides are currently labeled for use against this disease. However, efficacy may vary based on the disease level at the time of application, environmental conditions before and after application, spray coverage, active ingredient, and other factors.

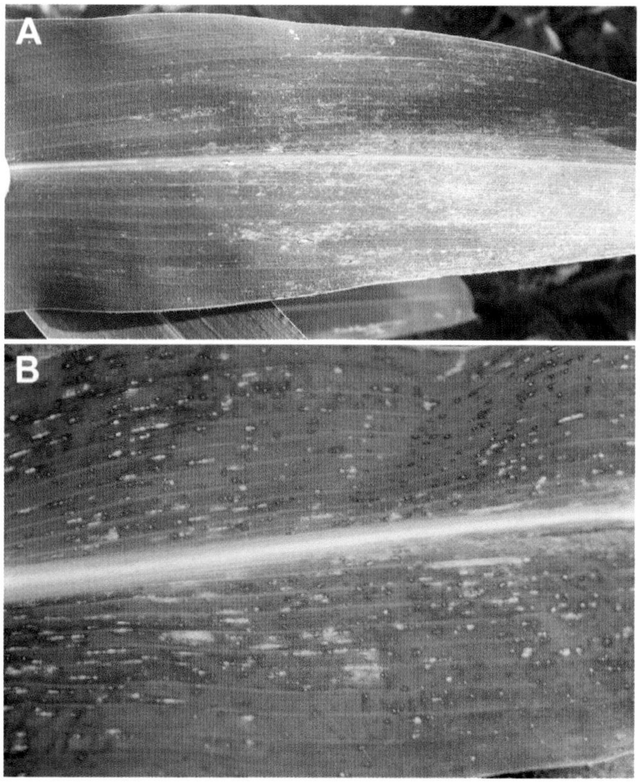

#Diagnostic Key Words

midseason, late season, wet, cool (race 3), warm (race 2), fieldwide, death, lesions, lower canopy

FIG. 4.64. A, "String of pearls" lesions, characteristic of northern corn leaf spot. **B,** Lesions produced by race 3 of the northern corn leaf spot fungus.

4.19 Physoderma Brown Spot and Stalk Rot

Fungus: *Physoderma maydis*

Physoderma brown spot and stalk rot is considered relatively unimportant in the United States and Canada, except in rare cases. The causal fungus can produce both foliar and stalk symptoms.

Symptoms and Signs

The lesions produced by Physoderma brown spot appear on midcanopy leaves from V12 through R1 (Fig. 4.65). Leaf lesions are numerous, very small (approximately ¼ inch [6 mm] in diameter), round to oval, and yellowish to brown; they usually form in bands across leaves. Dark-purple to black, oval spots usually occur on the midribs of leaves (Fig. 4.66)—a symptom that distinguishes Physoderma brown spot from other foliar diseases. Dark-purple, round spots may also occur on leaf sheaths, and they may or may not be associated with lesions on leaves.

FIG. 4.67. Physoderma stalk rot can cause plants to break at the lower nodes.

FIG. 4.65. Plants displaying symptoms of Physoderma brown spot.

FIG. 4.66. Physoderma brown spot lesions on the midrib of a leaf.

FIG. 4.68. Physoderma stalk rot lesions.

Physoderma stalk rot can cause the plant to break at one of the first three nodes above the soil (Fig. 4.67). The node at which breakage occurs has a blackish discoloration, and lesions and pith rot may be evident (Fig. 4.68). Microscopic examination of the symptomatic tissue reveals thousands of light-brown, round fungal structures.

Most Commonly Confused With

Common Rust (4.3) • Eyespot (4.8) • Southern Rust (4.22) • Pythium Stalk Rot (6.7) and other stalk rots (Chapter 6) • Lesion Mimic (8.3) • Purple Leaf Sheath (8.3) • Greensnap (8.3)

Physoderma leaf spots do not have dusty spores (characteristic of southern rust) or raised lesions with light centers (characteristic of eyespot). The lesions produced by purple leaf sheath appear only on the leaf sheaths; there are no leaf symptoms. Laboratory diagnosis may be necessary to confirm a stalk rot.

Favorable Conditions

The fungus overwinters in infected host tissue or infested soil and produces numerous spores under wet conditions; these spores are able to swim in free water. Infection of a leaf occurs in the whorl when water is present for an extended period. Because infection requires a combination of light, free water, and warm temperatures (75–85°F [24–30°C]), alternating bands of infected and noninfected tissue commonly develop on the leaf or plant. Younger plants are more susceptible to this disease but become more resistant with age.

Management

Management is not typically warranted for Physoderma brown spot and stalk rot.

Fungicides. Fungicides are labeled for control of Physoderma brown spot, but the availability of efficacy data is limited.

#Diagnostic Key Words

midseason, late season, wet, ponding/ wet soils (stalk rot), warm, fieldwide (brown spot), lodging, stalk lesions, lesions, middle canopy

4.20 Sorghum Downy Mildew

Oomycete: *Peronosclerospora sorghi*

Sorghum downy mildew is found wherever corn is grown. The disease is rare but can be problematic when susceptible hybrids are grown in the U.S. South.

Symptoms and Signs

The development of long, yellow or brown foliar lesions is a common symptom of sorghum downy mildew. Yellowing begins at the base of the leaf and stops abruptly at some point (Fig. 4.69). The yellowed area becomes larger on each successive leaf, from the bottom to the top of the plant. Additional symptoms include stunting, abnormal seed set, white stripes on leaves, narrow and erect leaves, leaf shredding, tassel deformation, barren ears, and ear shank elongation (Figs. 4.70 and 4.71). Fluffy white growth on the upper and lower leaf surfaces is another sign of infection by the causal pathogen (Fig. 4.72).

Most Commonly Confused With

Crazy Top (4.6)

To distinguish sorghum downy mildew from crazy top, plants should be observed for excessive tillering. Plants with crazy top also display rolling and twisting in the uppermost leaves.

FIG. 4.69. Yellow leaf lesions of sorghum downy mildew.

FIG. 4.70. White stripes on leaves caused by sorghum downy mildew.

FIG. 4.71. Narrow and erect leaves, characteristic of sorghum downy mildew.

FIG. 4.72. White fungal growth on a leaf, a sign of sorghum downy mildew.

Favorable Conditions

The pathogen overwinters in the soil and becomes active when soil temperatures warm to at least 68°F (20°C). Seedlings are infected systemically, and secondary infections result when the conidia that form on the leaves of infected plants are dispersed via wind to additional plants. Cool, wet weather is required for the development of conidia.

Management

Resistance. Resistant hybrids have been identified. Hybrids that emerge and establish quickly may also avoid becoming infected.

Cultural Practices. In regions in which sorghum downy mildew is problematic, rotation with or planting next to sorghum will increase the risk of disease development. Planting before the soil reaches 68°F (20°C) reduces the risk of seedling infection.

Fungicides. Most seed is treated with a systemic treatment of metalaxyl or mefenoxam, which can reduce disease risk.

Weed Management. Fields that contain the weed shattercane, which is a host of the pathogen, are at higher risk for this disease.

#Diagnostic Key Words

wet, warm, stunting, distortion, abnormal ears, lesions, leaf discoloration

Southern Corn
4.21 Leaf Blight

Fungus: *Bipolaris maydis*

There are three distinct races of the fungus that causes southern corn leaf blight (SCLB): race T, race O, and race C. The devastating leaf blight epidemic of 1970–1971 was caused by race T. It attacks only hybrids with Texas male-sterile cytoplasm, which are not commonly used in commercial production in the U.S. Midwest but may be used in other areas of the country. Race T also produces a toxin (T-toxin). Race O is most often observed in the United States and Canada; it infects hybrids with normal cytoplasm. Race C has been reported in Asia.

Symptoms and Signs

Race O of the causal fungus normally infects only the leaves, while race T can infect the leaves, husks, stalks, leaf sheaths, shanks, ears, and cobs. Foliar symptoms develop from VT through R4 (Fig. 4.73). Symptoms may appear at earlier growth stages in seed production fields.

Race O lesions are tan with reddish-brown margins, up to ¼ inch (6 mm) wide by 1 inch (2.5 cm) long, and somewhat rectangular. Race T lesions are rectangular to elliptical and ¼–½ inch (6–13 mm) wide by ¼–¾ inch (6–20 mm) long; they have reddish-brown margins that may be surrounded by chlorotic zones (Fig. 4.74).

Stalk and leaf infections initially produce purple spots, which develop tan-gray centers. Ear infections produce gray-black lesions on the husks that extend into the kernels (Fig. 4.75), appearing as a black, feltlike mold. Seedlings from infected kernels are often blighted.

Most Commonly Confused With

Anthracnose Leaf Blight (4.1) · Common Rust (4.3) · Gray Leaf Spot (4.10) · Northern Corn Leaf Spot (4.18)

To distinguish SCLB from other diseases, the size of the lesions should be considered, as well as

FIG. 4.73. Southern corn leaf blight lesions.

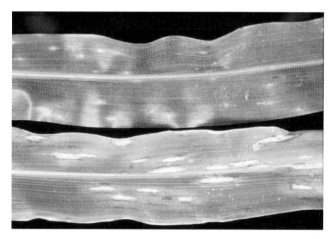

FIG. 4.74. Lesions of Race O (top) of the fungus that causes southern corn leaf blight, compared with lesions of Race T (bottom).

the general appearance of the lesions on leaves. Laboratory diagnosis may be needed to distinguish symptoms on some hybrids.

Favorable Conditions

Race O and T both overwinter as mycelium and spores in corn residue, and race T can also survive in the kernels. Spores are produced during warm, humid weather and spread by wind and splashing water. Race T specifically infects corn hybrids with Texas male-sterile cytoplasm, which are rarely used in the United States and Canada.

Warm, temperate and tropical climates are most conducive for disease development. Disease levels will likely increase during extended periods of cloudy weather with frequent rain showers.

Management

Resistance. Most hybrids are resistant to race T. Exceptions include hybrids and inbred lines that contain Texas male-sterile cytoplasm. Hybrids with normal cytoplasm are resistant to race T. Polygenic resistance is available for race T and race O.

Cultural Practices. Inoculum levels can be reduced by rotating crops and decreasing surface residue through tillage. If tillage is considered to decrease pathogen levels, efforts should be made to minimize soil erosion and maintain soil quality. In reduced-tillage systems, resistance and rotation are important disease management practices.

Fungicides. Fungicides are currently labeled for use against SCLB. However, efficacy may vary based on disease progression, environmental conditions (before and after application), spray coverage, active ingredient, and additional factors.

#Diagnostic Key Words

midseason, late season, wet, warm, fieldwide, stalk lesions (race T), lesions

FIG. 4.75. Ears infected with the fungus that causes southern corn leaf blight develop dark lesions on the husks.

4.22 Southern Rust

Fungus: *Puccinia polysora*

Southern rust is problematic in the southern United States but occurs less frequently in the midwestern and Great Plains states and in Ontario, Canada. In  2008, a new genetic variant (race) of the southern rust fungus was discovered in the United States that can cause disease on formerly resistant hybrids.

Symptoms and Signs

The southern rust fungus produces pustules that are orange to light brown, circular or oval, and about 1/16 inch (1.5 mm) long (Fig. 4.76). Pustules develop

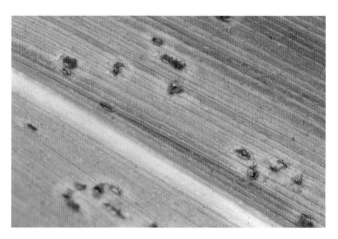

FIG. 4.76. Pustules of southern rust on the upper surface of a leaf.

FIG. 4.77. Numerous southern rust pustules densely packed on a leaf.

primarily on the upper leaf surface and are numerous and densely packed (Fig. 4.77). Many pustules appear to have failed to break through the epidermis on the leaf surface, but they eventually erupt. Chocolate-brown to black pustules may form around the original pustules as the season progresses.

Pustules may also appear on the stalks, husks, leaf sheaths, and ear shanks (Fig. 4.78).

Most Commonly Confused With

Common Rust (4.3) • Eyespot (4.8) • Physoderma Brown Spot (4.19)

Southern rust produces pustules that are bright orange, located predominantly on the upper leaf surface, and generally more densely clustered than those of common rust (Fig. 4.79). The pustules produced by common rust are also darker and more elongated than those produced by southern rust. Mixed infections of both rust fungi can occur on the same plant, which can confuse diagnosis.

Favorable Conditions

The causal fungus requires living plant tissue to survive, so when corn plants die, the host is lost. Thus, this fungus does not overwinter in northern

FIG. 4.78. Southern rust pustules on a leaf sheath.

areas. Each year, rust spores are blown north on wind currents from tropical areas and begin new infections when they land on leaves.

Rust fungi require short periods of leaf wetness to cause infection. Approximately 6 hours of dew usually provides enough moisture for infection and the onset of disease development. Disease development is favored by high humidity and temperatures around 80°F (27°C).

When conditions are favorable for rust development, the infection cycle repeats continually, resulting in secondary infections. A single pustule produces thousands of spores, which can infect the plant and quickly produce additional pustules under optimal conditions. If these cycles continue, disease intensity can reach an epidemic level in a short period of time.

Southern rust infrequently reaches the U.S. Corn Belt or Ontario in time to cause economic yield losses, because the level of inoculum must build up in southern North America and blow north.

Management

Resistance. Most hybrids are susceptible to southern rust, but a few resistant hybrids are available.

Cultural Practices. Cultural practices do not influence the development of rust, because the causal fungus does not survive in crop residue.

Fungicides. Fungicides are available and effective at managing this disease.

Diagnostic Key Words

midseason, late season, wet, warm, fieldwide, signs, stalk lesions, lesions, middle canopy, upper canopy

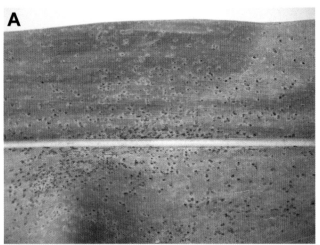

FIG. 4.79. A, Upper surface of a leaf with southern rust pustules protruding from it. **B**, Chlorotic flecking without pustules on the lower leaf surface helps distinguish common rust from southern rust.

4.23 Stewart's Disease

Bacterium: *Pantoea stewartii*

Stewart's disease is also called Stewart's wilt and bacterial wilt. The bacterium that causes it overwinters in the gut of the corn flea beetle and on grassy weeds. The corn flea beetle introduces the bacterium into corn plants as it feeds on them, carrying the pathogen from plant to plant. Stewart's disease is a major concern in seed corn production areas of the United States and Canada (southwestern Ontario), because many countries restrict the entrance of infected seed.

Stewart's disease used to be common in the United States and Canada, but very few confirmed cases have been documented since 2009. If you suspect your crop has this disease, submit a sample to a diagnostic laboratory for confirmation.

Symptoms and Signs

Stewart's disease has two distinct phases—wilt and leaf blight—and both phases are problematic when very susceptible dent corn hybrids or types of specialty corn are grown. The initial wilt phase affects seedlings and is most noticeable soon after emergence. Cutting a symptomatic seedling lengthwise reveals a discolored, rotted, or hollowed-out growing point. Because new growth is affected, wilting and even death can occur from the top of the plant down. Mature plants do not commonly exhibit wilt phase symptoms. The leaf blight phase often occurs later in the growing season after tasseling (pollination). Both phases produce foliar symptoms, which are caused by the pathogen being introduced during feeding of the corn flea beetle.

If the bacterium enters the stalk, systemic (whole-plant) infection can occur. The initial wilt phase results from the systemic infection of seedlings; however, systemic infection does not always cause the plant to wilt. Systemic infection can produce wilting and death of whole leaves, as well as stunting, bleached and dead tassels, discolored and dead vascular tissue, decayed cavities in stalk tissue, and plant death (Fig. 4.80). When cut, an infected stalk may ooze droplets of pale-yellow bacteria. In susceptible hybrids and specialty corn, a systemic infection can cause rapid wilting and death at any time before tasseling. Tillering can occur when seedling stalks are killed.

In the second phase, leaf blight lesions appear as pale-green to yellow streaks (Fig. 4.81). The streaks begin at the feeding sites of corn flea beetles, which resemble tiny scratches at the bases of lesions (Fig. 4.82). The streaks may have a water-soaked appearance, are from 1/16–1/2 inch (1.5–13.0 mm)

FIG. 4.80. Systemic (whole-plant) infection occurs if the bacterium that causes Stewart's wilt enters the stalk.

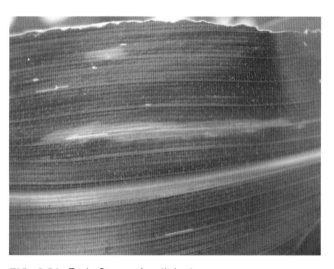

FIG. 4.81. Early Stewart's wilt lesions.

wide, and may run the entire length of the leaf (Fig. 4.83A). As the disease progresses, the streaks turn into brown lesions and the leaf tissue dies. The margins of lesions are usually wavy but generally follow the leaf veins (Fig. 4.83B). Entire leaves can be blighted late in the season.

FIG. 4.82. Feeding scar from a corn flea beetle.

Most Commonly Confused With

Diplodia Leaf Streak (4.7) • Goss's Wilt (4.9) • Northern Corn Leaf Blight (4.17) • Nitrogen Deficiency (8.1) • Drought (8.3) • High Temperatures (8.3) • Insect Injury (8.4)

The flea beetle feeding scar and resulting lesion are unique to Stewart's disease and help distinguish it from other diseases and disorders.

Favorable Conditions

The occurrence of Stewart's disease is strongly linked to the winter survival rate of the corn flea beetle and can be predicted based on winter temperatures. When the average winter temperature is above freezing, more beetles survive and the threat of the disease is therefore higher. Prediction models can be used to assess the risk of disease caused by beetle survival.

Several generations of corn flea beetle are produced throughout the summer; they acquire the bacterium from previously infected plants and spread it during feeding. Dry summer weather is conducive to corn flea beetle reproduction and activity.

The bacterium that causes Stewart's disease is also seedborne, but seed transmission is extremely rare.

FIG. 4.83. A, Streaklike lesions of Stewart's wilt. **B**, Elongated lesions run parallel to the leaf veins.

Management

Resistance. Most hybrids are resistant enough to Stewart's disease that no further management is required. However, a few inbred lines of seed corn are susceptible to the disease, and some specialty corn hybrids are very susceptible.

Cultural Practices. Most cultural practices do not affect the development and progression of Stewart's disease, because the pathogen survives in the corn flea beetle.

Fungicides. Fungicides are not effective against this bacterial disease.

Insect Management. If the population of flea beetles is extremely high, applying a foliar insecticide can reduce the population and the spread of disease at the beginning of the growing season. This scenario will occur only after a very mild winter, however. In seed production fields planted to susceptible inbreds, applying an insecticide on a more frequent basis may be necessary. Applying a systemic insecticide to the soil or seed has helped reduce early season disease levels by controlling the flea beetle population.

Weed Management. Weed management may have some benefit, because the corn flea beetle prefers grassy weeds and the damage to corn is highest in weedy fields.

4.24 Other Viruses

Virus disease distribution is difficult to document. If you suspect your crop has one of these diseases, submit a sample to a diagnostic laboratory for confirmation.

Corn Lethal Necrosis/ Maize Lethal Necrosis

When *Maize chlorotic mottle virus* (MCMV) infects corn simultaneously with a potyvirus such as *Maize dwarf mosaic virus* (MDMV), *Sugarcane mosaic virus* (SCMV), or *Wheat streak mosaic virus* (WSMV), a synergistic disease complex is formed. Known as corn lethal necrosis (also maize lethal necrosis), this disease complex can result in the rapid death of plants. Corn lethal necrosis occurs primarily in the arid western parts of the U.S. Corn Belt (Kansas and Nebraska).

Symptoms of this systemic disease include severe chlorosis and leaf mottling (Fig. 4.84), tissue death (beginning with the top leaves), and barren ears. The disease is most severe when plants are infected at the early growth stages.

FIG. 4.84. Chlorosis and leaf mottling caused by corn lethal necrosis.

Planting resistant cultivars is recommended for disease management. The level of resistance depends on the growth stage of the host at the time of infection.

#Diagnostic Key Words

death, leaf discoloration, abnormal ears

High Plains Disease

High plains disease (HPD) is caused by *Wheat mosaic virus* (WMoV) (previously referred to as *High plains virus*). HPD was described as a disease of corn in the early 1990s in areas of Colorado, Kansas, Nebraska, and Texas. HPD has also been found in the midwestern states.

Symptoms of HPD on corn include stunting, mosaic, and yellowing (Fig. 4.85). Long, red, longitudinal stripes can also be associated with HPD.

Corn infected with WMoV often occurs near wheat fields, and infection with this virus is usually accompanied by infection with *Wheat streak mosaic virus* (WSMV). Wheat curl mites transmit both of these viruses. Corn planted near wheat fields or in close proximity to volunteer wheat can be at increased risk of infection by WMoV. Corn planted near weeds such as yellow foxtail and green foxtail may also be at higher risk for infection.

Management strategies include planting resistant cultivars, controlling weeds, planting at a later date, and avoiding planting corn near wheat. Many sweet corn hybrids are highly susceptible to HPD.

#Diagnostic Key Words

stunting, leaf discoloration

FIG. 4.85. Mosaic and yellow streaks, characteristic of high plains disease.

Crown and Root Diseases

Fusarium Crown and Root Rot

5.1

Fungi: *Fusarium* species

Many species of *Fusarium* are commonly found in fields throughout the United States and Canada. In addition to causing Fusarium crown and root rot, some species also cause Fusarium stalk rot and ear rot of corn (sections 6.5 and 7.5, respectively).

Symptoms and Signs

Symptoms of Fusarium crown and root rot may occur throughout the growing season. A root infection is characterized by a root system that is small and discolored (slightly brown to black) or has rotted tips (Fig. 5.1). In younger plants, the mesocotyl is firm or shriveled and tan to pink.

If the infection progresses into the crown, the crown is slightly discolored or dark and rotted (Figs. 5.2 and 5.3), leading to leaf yellowing or purpling, stunting, and wilting, as well as symptoms of potassium deficiency and possibly death. Plants with severely rotted crowns may suddenly die when the weather becomes warm and sunny. A crown infection can persist well into the growing season, eventually resulting in stalk rot.

Symptoms of Fusarium crown rot may not be outwardly apparent, even though the crown and/or roots may be colonized and rotted.

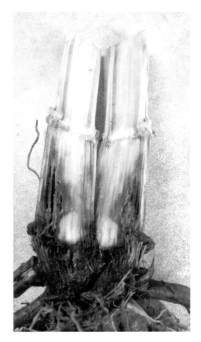

FIG. 5.2. Symptoms of Fusarium crown rot in the stalk tissue.

FIG. 5.1. Discolored roots caused by Fusarium root rot.

FIG. 5.3. Discoloration of the lower stalk and crown caused by Fusarium crown rot.

Most Commonly Confused With

Red Root Rot (5.3) • Other root rot diseases (Chapter 5) • Herbicide Injury (8.2) • Soil Crusting (8.3) • Insect Injury (8.4)

It may not be possible to diagnose Fusarium crown and root rot in the field. Laboratory diagnosis may be needed to distinguish among diseases and disorders with similar symptoms and signs.

Favorable Conditions

Fusarium crown and root rot may develop under a range of soil temperatures and moisture levels. Plants are often more susceptible to infection under stressful growth conditions, such as wet soils, cold temperatures, compacted soils, fertility problems, and herbicide injury. *Fusarium* species survive as mycelium or spores in the soil or plant residue, and they can also be seedborne. Infection occurs when the roots come into contact with inoculum.

Management

Cultural Practices. Providing good soil drainage and mitigating compaction may reduce disease severity.

Fungicides. Seed treatments can help to control early infections. However, the fungicide will not remain active long enough in the soil or the plant to manage the crown rot stage of the disease.

#Diagnostic Key Words

midseason, late season, wet, ponding/wet soils, patchy, poor emergence, stunting, wilting, death

5.2 Pythium Seedling Blight and Root Rot

Oomycetes: *Pythium* species

Pythium seedling blight and root rot is caused by many species of *Pythium*, and they are distributed across the United States and Canada.

Symptoms and Signs

Diseased plants often occur singly or in small patches in low-lying areas of the field that are prone to flooding (Fig. 5.4). Affected plants usually have delayed development and necrotic leaf margins, and they may appear yellowed and wilted (Fig. 5.5). Plants may also die, resulting in low stand counts. Digging in areas where emergence is inconsistent may reveal rotted seedlings that never broke through the soil.

The seminal roots and mesocotyl tissue are soft, water soaked, and dark colored in plants with Pythium seedling blight and root rot (Fig. 5.6). The rotted surface can be peeled off the outside of a seminal root, leaving the white inner root (Fig. 5.7).

FIG. 5.4. Stunting and uneven distribution of seedlings caused by Pythium seedling blight.

Most Commonly Confused With

Damage caused by nematodes (5.5, 5.6, 5.7) • Other root rot diseases (Chapter 5) • Herbicide Injury (8.2) • Soil Crusting (8.3) • Frost Damage (8.3) • Flooding (8.3) • Insect Injury (8.4)

It may not be possible to diagnose Pythium seedling blight and root rot in the field. Laboratory diagnosis may be needed to distinguish among diseases and disorders with similar symptoms and signs.

Favorable Conditions

The conditions that favor Pythium seedling blight and root rot include early planting, cold soil temperatures, and saturated soils. Low-lying fields with poor drainage are at the highest risk of developing Pythium root rot. Soil crusting and other factors that delay emergence can also enhance disease development.

Pythium species can produce oospores, which overwinter in crop residue and soil. When soil is flooded during the spring, these structures produce spores that infect plants. Oospores can also produce mycelium.

Unlike other root rots, Pythium root rot is not seedborne.

Management

Cultural Practices. Planting in cold, wet soils should be avoided to reduce infections by *Pythium* species that favor low temperatures. Thus, improving drainage and waiting for soils to warm before planting can help to control this disease. Soils under conservation tillage often have higher levels of soil moisture and lower soil temperatures—both factors that increase the risk of infection by *Pythium* species. If tillage is considered to improve drainage, conservation tillage practices should be implemented to maintain soil quality.

FIG. 5.5. Poorly developed plant with root discoloration caused by Pythium root rot.

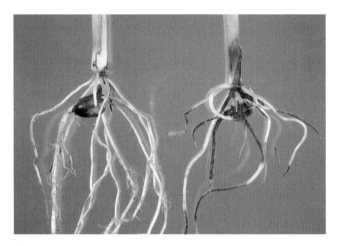

FIG. 5.6. Mesocotyl rot and root lesions, symptoms of Pythium root rot.

FIG. 5.7. Rotted outer surface has pulled away and exposed the inner root, characteristic of Pythium root rot.

Fungicides. The incidence of Pythium seedling blight is generally reduced by the seed treatment fungicides that are standard for all seed corn. Seed treatments may protect the stand in cool, wet conditions, but no seed treatment is effective against all species of *Pythium*. Mefenoxam, metalaxyl, and ethaboxam are effective against many *Pythium* species, but reduced sensitivity to mefenoxam and metalaxyl has also been documented. Quinone outside inhibitor (QoI) fungicides (strobilurins) may have limited activity against certain *Pythium* species.

#Diagnostic Key Words

early season, wet, ponding/wet soils, cool, patchy, poor emergence, wilting

5.3 Red Root Rot

Fungal disease complex: *Phoma terrestris* (synonym: *Pyrenochaeta terrestris*), *Pythium* species, and *Fusarium* species

Red root rot is a disease complex caused by multiple fungi.

Symptoms and Signs

Characteristic symptoms of red root rot include dark-red to pink roots (Fig. 5.8) and basal stalk discoloration (Fig. 5.9); these symptoms are usually observed as corn becomes physiologically mature. As the disease progresses, the red discoloration deepens to a purplish red and the root tissue shrivels.

FIG. 5.8. Red discoloration of the roots, characteristic of red root rot.

Reduced root mass, wilting, gray-green foliage and stalks, lodging, yield loss, reduced vigor, and premature plant death can all occur and are among the first indications of the disease.

Most Commonly Confused With

Fusarium Crown and Root Rot (5.1) · Fusarium Stalk Rot (6.5) · Gibberella Crown Rot and Stalk Rot (6.6)

Because the symptoms of red root rot are generally observed just before harvest, the disease is commonly confused with stalk rot diseases. The stalk discoloration produced by red root rot is typically darker red than that produced by Gibberella and Fusarium stalk rots. Even so, red root rot may be difficult to diagnose in the field, and laboratory diagnosis may be needed for confirmation.

Favorable Conditions

Moderate temperatures and high-yielding field environments (high plant populations, high soil fertility, and irrigation) provide the conditions conducive for disease development. The fungi survive in the soil and weakly parasitize many hosts. They can invade the root tissue later in the season, and as corn dries down, the colonization rate increases.

Infection by other pathogens may facilitate infection or increase the risk of red root rot developing.

Management

Management is rarely warranted for this disease.

Cultural Practices. Rotation to soybean may reduce development of the disease.

#Diagnostic Key Words

late season, wilting, lodging, death

FIG. 5.9. Basal stalk discoloration caused by red root rot.

5.4 Rhizoctonia Crown and Brace Root Rot

Fungus: *Rhizoctonia solani*

Rhizoctonia crown and brace root rot has been observed in a limited number of locations around the world, but it may remain undetected in other locations because of the lack of obvious symptoms. *Rhizoctonia solani* can also cause pre- and postemergence seedling diseases.

Symptoms and Signs

When aboveground symptoms occur, they include yellowing and stunting of infected plants (Fig. 5.10). On seedlings, oval, brown lesions may develop on the mesocotyl and seminal roots (Fig. 5.11). The mesocotyl may be firm, or it may be slightly collapsed. Seedlings may die when infections are severe.

More commonly, symptoms occur on mature plants as dark lesions on the roots. The roots disintegrate below the soil line. Patches of lodged plants may occur later in the season.

Most Commonly Confused With

Other root rot diseases (Chapter 5) • Herbicide Injury (8.2) • Soil Crusting (8.3)

It may be difficult to differentiate Rhizoctonia crown and brace root rot from other diseases and disorders, particularly at the early stages of plant growth. Laboratory analysis may be necessary for confirmation.

Favorable Conditions

Development of the causal fungus is not limited to a particular soil temperature or moisture range, although development is enhanced in aerated soils. Consequently, Rhizoctonia crown and brace root rot is generally more severe in crops planted in light and sandy soils and on the slopes of hills. The fungus survives in plant residue and soils as sclerotia.

Herbicide injury may also favor infection and disease development.

Management

Cultural Practices. Eliminating stress factors, such as the use of herbicides that cause injury to corn, can help reduce the likelihood the disease will

FIG. 5.10. Stunting and reduced vigor of plants caused by Rhizoctonia crown and brace root rot.

FIG. 5.11. Lesions on the mesocotyl, characteristic of Rhizoctonia crown and brace root rot.

develop. Rotation to soybean may not be beneficial for control of the pathogen, because soybean can be a host of the causal fungus. However, extending rotations with other nonhost crops tends to reduce disease. Good soil drainage and tillage to reduce residue may also be helpful. If tillage is considered to decrease residue, efforts should be made to minimize soil erosion and maintain soil quality.

Fungicides. Certain seed treatments can help to prevent disease.

Weed Management. Good weed management can help to reduce disease.

#Diagnostic Key Words

early season, late season, sandy soil, wet, ponding/wet soils, patchy, stunting, lodging

5.5 Root-Lesion Nematode

Pratylenchus species

The root-lesion nematode is widely distributed across the United States and Canada and can be found at very high populations in the soil. Of the many nematodes that feed on corn, the root-lesion nematode is thought to be most significant in terms of the damage it causes.

Symptoms and Signs

The root-lesion nematode is an endoparasite; it usually feeds inside the root and moves to new feeding sites within the root tissue. Belowground, lesions develop on the root tissue, and the roots may appear to be pruned (Fig. 5.12). Both the volume and weight of roots can be decreased. Aboveground symptoms can appear in patches within a field, with the most severe symptoms appearing in the centers of the patches. These symptoms include plant stunting and yellowing and produce yield losses

FIG. 5.12. Root damage caused by the root-lesion nematode.

(Fig. 5.13). In some cases, however, infected plants do not display any visible symptoms.

Feeding by the root-lesion nematode can provide other plant pathogens with entry points for infection. These pathogens may interact with the nematode and form a disease complex.

Most Commonly Confused With

Pythium Seedling Blight and Root Rot (5.2) • Damage caused by other nematodes (5.6, 5.7) • Nutrient Deficiency (8.1) • Drought (8.3) • Insect Injury (8.4)

Soil sampling and laboratory analyses are required to determine if root-lesion nematodes are causing observed symptoms. Nematodes should be extracted from both the roots and the soil to estimate the population of endoparasitic nematodes.

Favorable Conditions

Although root-lesion nematodes are present in many types of soil, sandy soil favors damage. Damage to crops can also be worse with warm soil temperatures in the spring. Nematodes cannot be eliminated from a field, but the population can be managed to reduce impact on the crop.

Management

Resistance. No resistant hybrids are commercially available.

Cultural Practices. Maintaining adequate soil fertility will minimize the likelihood of nutrient deficiency, which can predispose plants to nematode injury. Tillage and crop rotation can be useful strategies for reducing some nematode populations. If tillage is considered, efforts should be taken to minimize soil erosion and maintain soil quality.

Weed Management. Managing weeds will minimize nematode reproduction on weed hosts.

Nematicides. Soil-applied and seed treatment nematicides may be helpful but not economical in all cases.

#Diagnostic Key Words

sandy soils, patchy, stunting

FIG. 5.13. Yellowing and stunted growth—aboveground symptoms of damage caused by the root-lesion nematode.

5.6 Sting and Needle Nematodes

Belonolaimus and ***Longidorus*** species (respectively)

Nematodes from both genera are large; in fact, the needle nematode is the largest nematode that feeds on plants. Both sting and needle nematodes can be very destructive to corn, but injury is generally restricted to fields with soil composed of at least 70% sand.

Needle nematodes are typically associated with sandy soils, but distribution of both needle and sting nematodes is difficult to document. If you suspect your crop has nematode-related symptoms, submit a sample to a diagnostic laboratory for confirmation.

Symptoms and Signs

Crop injury can be severe when nematodes feed on roots early in corn development. Aboveground symptoms of nematode injury appear in patches within the field. Symptoms include stunting, yellowing, and wilting and lead to yield losses (Figs. 5.14 and 5.15).

Sting and needle nematodes feed from the outside of the root near the tip; they may cause root stunting, swelling, and discoloration, as well as a lack of smaller feeder roots (Fig. 5.16). The development of

FIG. 5.14. Stunting and yellowing of plants caused by the needle nematode.

FIG. 5.15. Patches of damage caused by the sting nematode.

FIG. 5.16. Root damage caused by the needle nematode.

symptoms can cause the roots to look like a bottle-brush (Fig. 5.17). When both sting and stubby-root nematodes (section 5.7) feed on the roots, the injury that results can be particularly severe.

Most Commonly Confused With

Root symptoms: Pythium Seedling Blight and Root Rot (5.2) • Damage caused by other nematodes (5.5, 5.7) • Herbicide Injury (8.2) • Insect Injury (8.4)

Aboveground symptoms: Nutrient and Fertilizer Disorders (8.1) • Drought (8.3)

Soil sampling and laboratory analysis are required to determine if sting and/or needle nematodes are causing observed symptoms.

Favorable Conditions

Generally, sting and needle nematodes are only problematic in soils with very high sand content. Continuous corn production favors population growth of the needle nematode, as does cool, wet soil. The needle nematode goes deeper into the soil when the surface soil is warm and dry, such as during the summer. Similarly, the sting nematode will move several feet down into the soil during the summer. Thus, the best time to sample for these nematodes is during the spring.

Management

Resistance. No resistant hybrids are commercially available.

Cultural Practices. Maintaining adequate soil fertility will minimize the likelihood of nutrient deficiency, which can predispose plants to nematode injury. Crop rotation to a nonhost plant can reduce the needle nematode population. Because adults can survive for 2 years, rotating away from corn for more than 1 year may help control the population. Soybean, cotton, and other plants are also hosts of the sting nematode, which reduces the effectiveness of rotating to these crops; rotation with alfalfa may be beneficial, however. The sting nematode dies quickly when a host plant is not present.

Weed Management. Managing weeds will minimize sting and needle nematode reproduction on weed hosts.

Nematicides. Soil-applied and seed treatment nematicides may be helpful but not economical in all cases.

#Diagnostic Key Words

sandy soil, wet, patchy, stunting, wilting

FIG. 5.17. Bottle-brush appearance of roots caused by the sting nematode.

5.7 Other Nematodes

Lance nematode: *Hoplolaimus galeatus*

Root-knot nematode: *Meloidogyne* species

Stubby-root nematode: *Paratrichodorus* species

Many other species of nematodes feed on corn, and several species can be present in one field at the same time.

Nematode distribution is difficult to document. If you suspect your crop has nematode-related symptoms, submit a sample to a diagnostic laboratory for confirmation.

Symptoms and Signs

Depending on the species, a nematode may feed on the outside (ectoparasitic) or the inside (endoparasitic) of the root or both (Fig. 5.18). Aboveground symptoms may appear in patches within the field; they include uneven plant height, stunting, yellowing, and early maturity and can produce yield losses (Fig. 5.19).

The roots can be pruned, discolored, and swollen, and they may display an abundance of fibrous roots or galls (Figs. 5.20 and 5.21). Sometimes, plants can be infected but not show any symptoms.

Most Commonly Confused With

Root symptoms: Pythium Seedling Blight and Root Rot (5.2) • Damage caused by other nematodes (5.5, 5.6) • Herbicide Injury (8.2) • Insect Injury (8.4)

Aboveground symptoms: Nutrient and Fertilizer Disorders (8.1) • Drought (8.3)

Soil sampling and laboratory analyses (including the extraction of nematodes from plants' roots) are required to determine if these nematodes are causing observed symptoms.

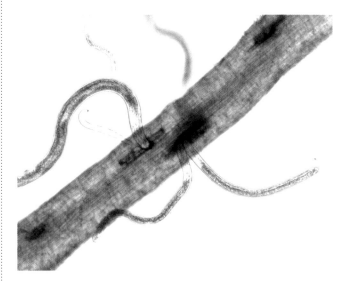

FIG. 5.18. Ectoparasitic feeding by lance nematodes.

FIG. 5.19. Field symptoms of damage caused by the stubby-root nematode.

FIG. 5.20. Root damage caused by the stubby-root nematode.

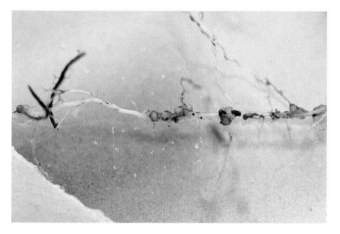

FIG. 5.21. Root damage caused by the root-knot nematode.

Favorable Conditions

Sandy soils are most favorable for nematodes, but these pathogens can also live in and cause damage to crops grown in other soil types. Nematode feeding can create entry points for other pathogens; high temperatures and the lack of moisture can exacerbate symptoms of nematode feeding.

Management

Resistance. No resistant hybrids are commercially available.

Cultural Practices. Maintaining adequate soil fertility will minimize the likelihood of nutrient deficiency, which can predispose plants to nematode injury. The effectiveness of rotation and tillage is species dependent; several nematodes can feed on many host plants, which minimizes the effectiveness of rotation.

Weed Management. Managing weeds will minimize the alternative hosts available to nematodes.

Nematicides. Soil-applied and seed treatment nematicides may be helpful but not economical in all cases.

#Diagnostic Key Words

sandy soil, dry, warm, patchy, stunting

Stalk Rots

6.1 Anthracnose Stalk Rot

Fungus: *Colletotrichum graminicola*

Anthracnose stalk rot is probably the most consistently damaging stalk rot affecting corn in the eastern United States and in Ontario, Canada. It is caused by the same fungus that causes anthracnose leaf blight (section 4.1); however, anthracnose stalk rot does not result directly from anthracnose leaf blight and vice versa. Anthracnose stalk rot is sometimes referred to as Anthracnose top dieback because of the symptoms it causes, but top dieback is a different phase of the same disease.

Symptoms and Signs

Symptoms of anthracnose stalk rot are usually prevalent around physiological maturity. Infection results in disintegration of the pith tissue, which leaves the vascular bundles intact but causes the interior of the stalk to appear shredded (Fig. 6.1). The pith is also typically discolored, turning dark brown beginning at the nodes.

In addition, anthracnose stalk rot causes a distinctive blackening of the stalk rind. Initially, these blackened areas are composed of narrow, water-soaked lesions, but they turn very dark and shiny as the growing season progresses (Fig. 6.2). The lesions may coalesce to form large, black blotches or streaks. This discoloration may appear across the entire stalk.

Plants can be infected during the vegetative growth stages, and some plants may die before pollination occurs. However, the disease usually does not appear until late in the season and can result in lodging.

The top dieback symptoms usually occur from stage R4 on. A yellowed, purple, or dead flag leaf surrounds the emerged tassel, and affected plants are randomly distributed through the field (Fig. 6.3). The characteristic black anthracnose lesions develop on the outside of the stalk at the top of an infected plant and can be observed when the leaf sheath is peeled back (Fig. 6.4). Under moist conditions, a pink, jellylike substance exudes from the lesions. This substance is composed of anthracnose spores in a jellylike matrix produced in an acervulus, which is a black, spiny structure visible with a 30× hand lens. When the stalk is split, the pith appears rotted or discolored in the upper internodes.

FIG. 6.1. Disintegration of pith tissue, a symptom of anthracnose stalk rot.

FIG. 6.2. Black lesions on the stalk, symptomatic of anthracnose stalk rot.

Most Commonly Confused With

Bacterial Stalk Rot (6.2) • Other stalk rot diseases (Chapter 6) • Environmental Conditions (8.3) • Insect Injury (8.4)

Other diseases and factors such as environmental stress and insect injury can cause the tops of plants to die back. Anthracnose stalk rot typically produces shiny, dark lesions on the stalk rind. Other stalk rots do not typically produce these kinds of lesions on the stalk.

FIG. 6.3. Symptoms of anthracnose top dieback.

FIG. 6.4. Anthracnose lesions develop on the outside of the stalk at the top of the plant and can be observed when the leaf sheath is peeled back.

Favorable Conditions

At the beginning of the growing season, inoculum is produced from infested corn residue, which is the primary overwintering source for the pathogen. Spores are spread to plants in a variety of ways, including wind and rain. Once spores contact the plant tissue, they germinate and penetrate the cells. Infection can occur multiple times during the season, and any plant part can be infected, including the roots, crown, stalk, and leaves.

Anthracnose stalk rot occurs when the fungus infects the plant through the roots or when spores splash onto the stalk and then enter the plant through wounds and leaf scars. Insects may also carry the spores and introduce them through feeding wounds. Spores produced from leaf blight lesions can serve as a secondary source of inoculum for stalk rot.

Anthracnose occurs more severely when corn follows corn in the same field, especially in reduced tillage. Occurrences of the stalk rot and the leaf blight are not related; however, top dieback onset and stalk rot severity may be linked.

Management

Resistance. Resistance to anthracnose stalk rot is available in some hybrids. Also, hybrids with strong stalks are less susceptible to lodging. Hybrids that are more resistant to foliar diseases may be less at risk of developing stalk rot, since the stress caused by leaf blight increases susceptibility to stalk rot.

Cultural Practices. Crop rotation will reduce the level of inoculum, although sorghum and several weeds are hosts of the fungus. Tillage will also reduce inoculum, but it may move inoculum into the root zone and cause a root infection. Ensuring balanced fertilization, maintaining appropriate plant populations, planting adapted hybrids, and providing good drainage all reduce the stresses that predispose plants to stalk rot. Early harvest prevents plants from lodging before the grain is harvested.

#Diagnostic Key Words

late season, wet, ponding/wet soils, warm, patchy (stalk rot), scattered (top dieback), lodging (stalk rot), death, signs, stalk lesions, rotting stalk interior

6.2 Bacterial Stalk Rot

Bacteria: *Erwinia* species

Bacterial stalk rot is a generally minor disease, but it can be problematic in seed corn. Symptoms often develop in the upper stalk (bacterial top rot) following hail damage.

Symptoms and Signs

Bacterial stalk rot usually causes decay of one or more internodes above the soil. The outer stalk and the pith become slimy, soft, brown, and water soaked (Fig. 6.5), and the decayed tissue usually has a

FIG. 6.5. Rotting pith and rind, characteristic of bacterial stalk rot.

FIG. 6.6. Twisting and breaking caused by bacterial stalk rot.

strong odor. The stalk typically twists and falls over (Fig. 6.6), but the plant may remain green for several weeks because the vascular tissue is not destroyed. In some cases, the leaves that form the whorl die before tasseling, and affected leaves can be easily pulled from the whorl.

Bacterial stalk rot can occur anytime during the season, unlike most other stalk rots, which appear post-tasseling. However, the main symptoms of bacterial stalk rot usually occur midseason.

Top rot symptoms include leaf wilting in the upper canopy (Fig. 6.7) and a rot that can make the plant collapse if it spreads downward.

Most Commonly Confused With

Anthracnose Stalk Rot (6.1) • **Pythium Stalk Rot (6.7)**

The sour smell from infected plants can help differentiate bacterial stalk rot from other stalk rots.

Favorable Conditions

Erwinia species overwinter in soil and corn stalk residue and are dispersed by splashing water. Bacterial stalk rot typically occurs when infested water is trapped in the whorls and behind the leaf

FIG. 6.7. Wilted top leaves, symptomatic of bacterial top rot.

sheaths. This can happen after an extended period of flooding with high temperatures and high humidity or when corn is irrigated with pond, ditch, or other surface water. Infection can also occur through natural openings and wounds. *Erwinia* species also cause diseases in many other host plants.

Management

Management of this disease is rarely warranted, but when it is, the following options should be considered.

Resistance. Some hybrids are more susceptible to bacterial stalk rot than others. Hybrids with strong stalks are less susceptible to lodging.

Cultural Practices. Residue should be incorporated during the fall to reduce inoculum. Ensuring balanced fertilization, maintaining appropriate plant populations, and providing good drainage will reduce the stresses that predispose plants to stalk rot.

#Diagnostic Key Words

early season, midseason, late season, wounding, wet, ponding/wet soils, warm, scattered, wilting (stalk rot), lodging (stalk rot), death, rotting stalk interior

6.3 Charcoal Rot

Fungus: *Macrophomina phaseolina*

Charcoal rot is found throughout the United States and southwestern Ontario, Canada. It may be more problematic in the U.S. South and during years when plants are under heat and drought stress. The causal fungus has many host plants and may affect crops that are rotated with corn, including soybean.

Symptoms and Signs

Charcoal rot causes the pith and stalk rind to appear a silvery gray because of the development of numerous black microsclerotia (Fig. 6.8). The pith tissue is disintegrated and peppered with microsclerotia, which gives the vascular tissue a granular, gray appearance (Fig. 6.9). Plants near maturity are most likely to become infected.

FIG. 6.8. Stalk pith appears silvery gray because of the development of microsclerotia—a sign of charcoal rot.

Most Commonly Confused With

Diplodia Stalk Rot (6.4) • **Fusarium Stalk Rot (6.5)** • **Gibberella Stalk Rot (6.6)**

The presence of microsclerotia in the pith distinguishes charcoal rot from other stalk rots.

Favorable Conditions

Charcoal rot is more severe when growing conditions are hot and dry, but symptoms may be observed in years with normal conditions, as well. The fungus overwinters as microsclerotia in crop residue and soil and infects plants through the roots and lower stems. Charcoal rot may be more prevalent in fields where previously infected corn or soybean residue is present. This disease usually appears first in the driest areas of a field, such as sandy areas, terrace tops, and headlands compacted by equipment traffic.

The pathogen has many alternative crop and weed hosts.

Management

Resistance. Hybrids with resistance to charcoal rot may be available, and those with strong stalks are less susceptible to lodging. Hybrids that are more resistant to foliar disease may also be at less risk for developing stalk rot, because the stress caused by leaf blight increases susceptibility to stalk rot.

Cultural Practices. Crop rotation may not be entirely effective at managing charcoal rot, because microsclerotia can survive more than 1 year in soil and host crops include soybean, sorghum, and alfalfa. Providing adequate irrigation is important in dry years (where applicable). Ensuring balanced fertilization, maintaining appropriate plant populations, and providing good drainage reduce the stresses that predispose plants to stalk rot. Early harvesting is also an option to avoid losses caused by lodging.

Weed Management. Effective weed management can eliminate alternative hosts of the pathogen.

#Diagnostic Key Words

late season, dry, warm, patchy, signs, stalk lesions, rotting stalk interior, lodging, death

FIG. 6.9. Shredded pith and microsclerotia caused by charcoal rot.

6.4 Diplodia Stalk Rot

Fungus: *Stenocarpella maydis*

Diplodia stalk rot is caused by the same fungus that causes Diplodia ear rot (section 7.4). Conservation tillage has increased the prevalence of this disease.

Symptoms and Signs

Diplodia stalk rot can be identified by the development of numerous small, black pycnidia (about the size of a pinhead) embedded in the rinds of the lower internodes of the stalk (Fig. 6.10). Under very wet conditions, white mold may develop on the stalk surface. Inside the stalk, the tissue is discolored and shredded (Fig. 6.11).

Diplodia stalk rot is sometimes initiated at the ear shank when the ear is infected by the causal fungus. More obvious symptoms occur when plants suddenly die before the grain reaches maturity. Rotted stalks can be soft when pinched, and lodging can occur when plants snap at the nodes.

Most Commonly Confused With

Charcoal Rot (6.3) · Fusarium Stalk Rot (6.5) · Gibberella Stalk Rot (6.6)

The presence of pycnidia on the lower stalk distinguishes Diplodia stalk rot from Fusarium stalk rot (Fig. 6.12). Diplodia stalk rot can be distinguished from Gibberella stalk rot in that the pycnidia are not easily scraped off; also, a pink discoloration is generally evident inside the stalk of an infected plant. Microsclerotia are visible when charcoal rot is present, and these structures can be easily confused with pycnidia. Laboratory confirmation may be necessary to accurately identify Diplodia stalk rot.

Favorable Conditions

The pathogen overwinters on corn residue and can also survive in seed. Pycnidia produce spores during wet weather, and the spores spread by splashing water and wind. Infection can occur

FIG. 6.10. Pycnidia embedded in a lower internode, a sign of Diplodia stalk rot.

FIG. 6.11. Lesions and shredded pith caused by Diplodia stalk rot.

FIG. 6.12. Lesions and pycnidia, characteristic symptoms and signs of Diplodia stalk rot.

through the crown, roots, mesocotyl, and lower nodes. Insects may also possibly carry the spores and introduce them through feeding wounds.

Diplodia stalk rot is favored by dry conditions early in the season followed by warm, wet conditions after silking.

Management

Resistance. Hybrids are available with good resistance to Diplodia stalk rot, and those with strong stalks are less susceptible to lodging. Hybrids that are more resistant to foliar disease may also be at less risk of developing stalk rot, because the stress caused by leaf blight increases susceptibility to stalk rot.

Cultural Practices. Diplodia stalk rot is more severe in corn planted following corn in the same field, so rotation and tillage should be implemented to reduce levels of inoculum. If tillage is used to decrease pathogen levels, efforts should be taken to minimize soil erosion and maintain soil quality. In reduced-tillage systems, resistance and rotation are very important disease management practices. Ensuring balanced fertilization, maintaining appropriate plant populations, and providing good drainage reduce the stresses that predispose plants to stalk rot. Early harvesting is also an option to avoid losses caused by lodging.

#Diagnostic Key Words

late season, lodging, death, signs, stalk lesions, rotting stalk interior, patchy

6.5 Fusarium Stalk Rot

Fungi: *Fusarium* species

Fusarium stalk rot is caused by several *Fusarium* species, but *Fusarium verticillioides* is the primary pathogen. This disease is one of the most common stalk rots affecting corn in the United States and Canada.

Symptoms and Signs

Fusarium stalk rot causes internal shredding and may cause discoloration of the stalk tissue, as well as external brown streaks on the lower internodes (Figs. 6.13 and 6.14). The rotted pith tissue may become discolored and turn a pale-pink to salmon color. More obvious symptoms occur when plants suddenly die before the grain reaches maturity. The leaves wilt and die, turning dull green or grayish, and the stalks are straw colored. Rotted stalks can be soft when pinched, and stalk rot may go unnoticed if pith deterioration is the only symptom. Lodging can also occur when plants snap at the nodes.

This disease may begin soon after pollination, but symptoms may not appear until late in the season.

FIG. 6.13. Shredded stalk tissue, a symptom of Fusarium stalk rot.

Most Commonly Confused With

Red Root Rot (5.3) • **Charcoal Rot (6.3)** • **Diplodia Stalk Rot (6.4)** • **Gibberella Stalk Rot (6.6)**

The lack of pycnidia on the lower stalks distinguishes Fusarium stalk rot from Diplodia stalk rot. Laboratory confirmation may be necessary to accurately identify Fusarium stalk rot.

Favorable Conditions

Fusarium fungi overwinter as mycelia in corn residue and other dead plant residue. Spores are spread by wind and splashing water, and infection occurs through the roots, wounds in stalks, and leaf nodes. *Fusarium verticillioides* is often found growing in healthy stalks and may cause rot only under certain conditions. This fungus is also commonly found in corn seed.

Warm, dry weather favors disease development. Other hosts include sorghum, wheat, cotton, soybean, and sugarcane.

Management

Resistance. Resistance to Fusarium stalk rot is available in commercial hybrids, and those with strong stalks are less susceptible to lodging. Hybrids that are more resistant to foliar disease may also be less at risk of developing stalk rot, since the stress caused by leaf blight increases susceptibility to stalk rot.

Cultural Practices. Rotation and tillage can reduce levels of inoculum. If tillage is considered to decrease pathogen levels, efforts should be made to minimize soil erosion and maintain soil quality. Ensuring balanced fertilization, maintaining appropriate plant populations, and providing good drainage reduce the stresses that predispose plants to stalk rot. Early harvesting is also an option to avoid losses caused by lodging.

#Diagnostic Key Words

late season, dry, warm, patchy, wilting, lodging, death, stalk lesions, rotting stalk interior

FIG. 6.14. Dark lesions and external brown streaks on the lower internode, symptoms of Fusarium stalk rot.

6.6 Gibberella Crown Rot and Stalk Rot

Fungus: *Fusarium graminearum*
(synonym: *Gibberella zeae*)

Gibberella stalk rot is common in the northern United States and in Canada. The pathogen also causes Gibberella ear rot (section 7.6) on corn and Fusarium head blight on wheat and barley.

Symptoms and Signs

Small, round, black fungal bodies (perithecia) may occur on internodes and nodes. These are the fruiting structures of the fungus, and they can be easily scraped off the stalk with a thumbnail (Fig. 6.15). Dark streaks may appear on the lower internodes. Inside the stalk, the rotted pith is usually light to dark pink and appears shredded (Fig. 6.16). More obvious symptoms occur when plants suddenly die before the grain reaches maturity. The leaves wilt and die, turning dull green or grayish, and the stalks appear straw colored. Rotted stalks can be soft when pinched, and stalk rot may go unnoticed if pith deterioration is the only symptom. Lodging can also occur when plants snap at the nodes.

Stalks and ears infected by *Fusarium graminearum* can contribute to mycotoxin contamination of corn that is harvested as silage and used for animal fodder. Deoxynivalenol (DON, vomitoxin) and zearalenone are the principal mycotoxins produced by this fungus. Cattle are tolerant of moderate levels of deoxynivalenol, but breeding animals that consume zearalenone can experience infertility and abortion.

Most Commonly Confused With

Red Root Rot (5.3) • Charcoal Rot (6.3) • Diplodia Stalk Rot (6.4) • Fusarium Stalk Rot (6.5)

The fruiting structures of the fungus that causes Gibberella stalk rot can be easily scraped off the stalk, while those of the fungus that causes Diplodia stalk rot are embedded in the rind and cannot be easily scraped off. Also, a pink discoloration is generally evident inside the stalk of an infected plant. Laboratory analysis may be necessary to distinguish Gibberella stalk rot from other stalk rots.

FIG. 6.15. Perithecia produced by the fungus that causes Gibberella stalk rot can be easily scraped off by a thumbnail.

FIG. 6.16. Pink discoloration and shredding inside the pith, characteristic of Gibberella stalk rot.

Favorable Conditions

The fungus overwinters in corn residue and sometimes in seed. Spores are produced during warm, wet weather and spread by wind and splashing water. Infection occurs through the roots, wounds in the stalks, and leaf nodes. Disease development is favored by the occurrence of plant stress and warm, wet conditions 2–3 weeks after silking.

Management

Resistance. Genetic resistance to Gibberella crown rot and stalk rot has been observed. Hybrids with strong stalks are less susceptible to lodging but may be susceptible to pith deterioration. Hybrids that are more resistant to foliar disease may also be less at risk of developing stalk rot, because the stress caused by leaf blight increases susceptibility to stalk rot.

Cultural Practices. Crop rotation and tillage will reduce the buildup of inoculum. Ensuring balanced fertilization, maintaining appropriate plant populations, practicing adequate insect control, and providing good drainage reduce the stresses that predispose plants to stalk rot. Early harvesting is also an option to avoid losses caused by lodging.

#Diagnostic Key Words

late season, wet, warm, patchy, wilting, lodging, death, signs, stalk lesions, rotting stalk interior

6.7 Pythium Stalk Rot

Oomycete: *Pythium aphanidermatum*

Pythium stalk rot is infrequently observed and considered of minor importance on corn in the United States and Canada.

Symptoms and Signs

Pythium stalk rot usually causes decay of the first internode above the soil (Fig. 6.17). The rind and the pith become soft, brown, and water soaked (Fig. 6.18). The stalk typically twists and falls over,

FIG. 6.17. Lesion at the base of the stalk, symptomatic of Pythium stalk rot.

FIG. 6.18. Rotted pith and rind, characteristic of Pythium stalk rot.

but the plant may remain green for several weeks because the vascular tissue is not destroyed.

Pythium stalk rot can occur anytime during the season, unlike most other stalk rots, which appear after tasseling.

Most Commonly Confused With

Physoderma Stalk Rot (4.19) · **Bacterial Stalk Rot (6.2)**

Pythium stalk rot does not typically produce the odor associated with bacterial stalk rot. Plants affected by Physoderma stalk rot will snap cleanly and not exhibit the twisting that characterizes Pythium stalk rot. Even so, laboratory diagnosis may be necessary to distinguish Pythium stalk rot from Physoderma stalk rot.

Favorable Conditions

Pythium stalk rot occurs predominantly during prolonged periods of hot, wet, or very humid weather. Poor soil drainage and high soil moisture are required for disease development. Disease incidence may be higher with overhead irrigation, especially when pond or stagnant water is used.

Management

Management is rarely warranted for this disease, but when it is, the following options should be considered.

Resistance. Some hybrids are more susceptible than others to Pythium stalk rot. Hybrids with strong stalks are less susceptible to lodging.

Cultural Practices. Ensuring balanced fertilization, maintaining appropriate plant populations, and providing good drainage reduce the stresses that predispose plants to stalk rot.

#Diagnostic Key Words

early season, midseason, late season, wet, ponding/wet soils, warm, scattered, lodging, death, rotting stalk interior

Ear Rots

Mycotoxins are toxic by-products of some of the fungi that cause ear and stalk rots, including *Aspergillus*, *Fusarium*, and *Gibberella* species (Fig. 7.1). These toxins are produced during fungal infection and are not living organisms. When animals feed on plant material contaminated with mycotoxins, a range of health issues can occur, including feed refusal, poor weight gain, reduced reproduction, and death.

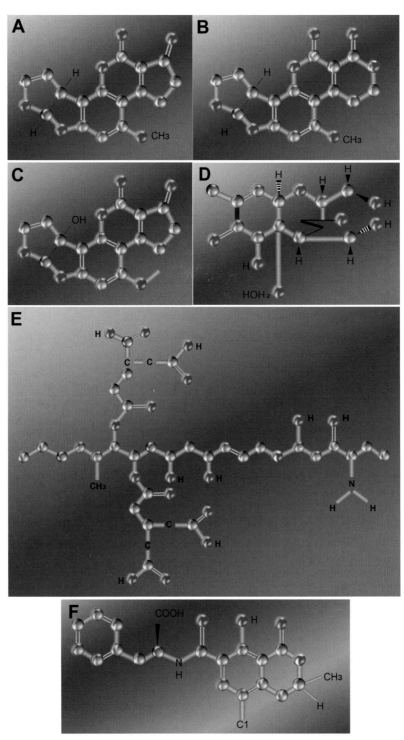

FIG. 7.1. Structures of common fungal mycotoxins: **A**, Aflatoxin B1; **B**, Aflatoxin G1; **C**, Aflatoxin M1; **D**, Deoxynivalenol; **E**, Fumonisin B1; **F**, Ochratoxin A.

Often, farmers and crop advisors incorrectly believe that they can kill or remove mycotoxins from grain, which is not the case. Mycotoxins are extremely stable in grain and plants, and treatments using heat, freezing, and chemicals will not typically degrade these compounds.

Mycotoxins are found at higher levels in broken grain particles known as fines, and it is possible to screen or clean grain to remove these particles. Coring a bin can also help reduce mycotoxins if affected grain accumulates in this area. None of these practices removes mycotoxins directly from grain but rather removes grain affected by mycotoxins.

Testing for Mycotoxins

Sample collection and preparation are extremely important to accurately test for mycotoxins in grain and silage. Several samples should be taken from different areas within the silage mass or grain, and then they should be combined into one larger sample and submitted for analysis. Sampling several different times from a moving stream of grain while the grain is being loaded or unloaded is the preferred method for sample collection. Farmers should not put potentially contaminated grain into bins if possible, and they should be aware of the potential dangers and exercise caution if they must enter a bin. The U.S. Department of Agriculture (USDA) provides specific recommendations and methods for sampling in Book I of its *Grain Inspection Handbook* (available online at www.gipsa.usda.gov/fgis/handbook/gihbk1_inspec.aspx); following these practices will ensure that the sample tested accurately represents the grain population. The Canadian Grain Commission provides grain-sampling procedures online (www.grainscanada.gc.ca).

Mycotoxins can be assessed using several different chemical and immunocapture technologies, but analyzing them can be a challenge because of their complex nature. It is important not to rely solely on visual methods (such as the black light test) for confirmation of mycotoxins, because visual test results can be inconsistent. Instead, samples should be sent to a professional laboratory for analysis.

7.2 Aspergillus Ear Rot and Aflatoxin

Fungi: *Aspergillus flavus,*
Aspergillus parasiticus, and other
Aspergillus species

Aspergillus ear rot can be caused by several species of *Aspergillus.* Two of them, *Aspergillus flavus* and *Aspergillus parasiticus,* produce aflatoxin—a carcinogen and the most well-known mycotoxin in corn.

Aspergillus flavus is the most common *Aspergillus* species associated with Aspergillus ear rot and aflatoxin production in U.S. corn. The U.S. Food and Drug Administration (FDA) has issued regulatory guidelines for safe levels of aflatoxin in the corn used for foods and animal feeds (available online at www.ngfa.org/wp-content/uploads/NGFAComplianceGuide-FDARegulatoryGuidanceforMycotoxins8-2011.pdf).

Aspergillus ear rot and aflatoxin rarely occur in Canada. Even so, several government agencies provide inspection services and have issued regulations regarding mycotoxin limits. The Canadian Grain Commission regulates the grain-handling industry (www.grainscanada.gc.ca—select English or French tab), and the Canadian Food Inspection Agency regulates food safety, animal health, and plant health (www.inspection.gc.ca—select English or French tab). In addition, Health Canada has issued guidelines for allowable mycotoxin levels in foods (available online at www.hc-sc.gc.ca/fn-an/securit/chem-chim/contaminants-guidelines-directives-eng.php).

Symptoms and Signs

The fungus that causes Aspergillus ear rot appears as an olive-green, powdery mold on the surfaces of kernels (Fig. 7.2). Generally, the fungus is observed on just a few kernels and most frequently at the ear tip, but it can be observed anywhere on the ear (Figs. 7.3 and 7.4). Often, infected kernels are brownish, lightweight, and shrunken. Visible mold

FIG. 7.2. Olive-green mold on an ear, a sign of Aspergillus ear rot.

FIG. 7.3. Dusty mold on an ear produced by the fungus that causes Aspergillus ear rot.

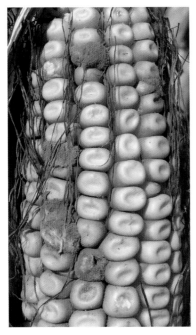

FIG. 7.4. Mold on kernels, a sign of Aspergillus ear rot.

and rotted kernels are most often associated with insect injury or other damage. However, visibly intact, normal-looking kernels may also be infected and have accumulated aflatoxin.

The absence of visible mold on the ear does not guarantee that it is free of aflatoxin. The only way to determine aflatoxin presence and level is by submitting adequate and representative grain samples to a lab that tests for aflatoxin using accredited procedures.

Most Commonly Confused With

Cladosporium Ear Rot (7.3) • Nigrospora Ear Rot (7.7) • Penicillium Ear Rot (7.8) • Trichoderma Ear Rot (7.9)

The mold associated with Aspergillus ear rot is more olive green than the bluish-green and gray-green molds associated with Trichoderma and Penicillium ear rots, respectively.

Favorable Conditions

Infection of corn by *Aspergillus flavus* and consequent disease development are both favored by hot (greater than 86°F [30°C]), humid, and dry conditions at pollination and during grain fill. Drought and high temperatures (80–105°F [26.5–40.5°C]) during grain fill are also the most common factors associated with preharvest aflatoxin production. A period of warm nights (greater than 70°F [21°C]) may also increase the risk of ear rot development and aflatoxin contamination.

Symptoms of Aspergillus ear rot usually appear first or are most severe in corn planted on hillsides and in sandy soils, where symptoms of drought initially occur. Other stresses that can predispose a crop to contamination include high plant populations and nitrogen deficiency.

The fungus that causes Aspergillus ear rot overwinters in soil, in plant residue, or on stored corn, but the disease is not seedborne. Spores are spread by wind and insects. Infection occurs through insect wounds and other types of wounds, as well as through the silks. Fungal growth and aflatoxin production occur as the kernel dries down; the fungus can produce aflatoxin until corn grain dries to 15% moisture.

Management

Resistance. Resistance to ear rots varies among hybrids. Complete resistance is not available, and many hybrids are susceptible.

Cultural Practices. Inoculum survives in the soil and is not readily reduced through crop rotation and tillage. Recommendations include maintaining adequate nitrogen fertility, avoiding planting at high populations, and improving conditions to prevent drought stress in areas in which the disease is prevalent.

Insect Management. Insect management through applying insecticides and using Bt hybrids can help to reduce potential pathogen entry points. Doing so may not prevent aflatoxin contamination, however.

Biological Control. Biocontrol products are available that contain strains of *Aspergillus flavus* that do not produce aflatoxin. They are applied prior to stage VT so that they colonize the corn and exclude colonization by naturally occurring aflatoxin-producing strains. These products have been used in the southern United States to reduce aflatoxin contamination of grain. Although these products can reduce aflatoxin levels, they do not typically eliminate aflatoxin. Moreover, efficacy depends on timing, application rate, and weather conditions before and after application. In sum, biocontrols should be used in conjunction with other management approaches.

Scouting. Fields in the dent stage should be scouted to identify areas with Aspergillus ear rot. These areas should be harvested as soon as possible to prevent further development of mold and mycotoxins. Aflatoxin levels may be high even if only a few kernels show signs of Aspergillus ear rot. Therefore, any field in which the disease is found should be managed using the harvest and postharvest recommendations outlined in the following sections.

Harvest. A properly adjusted combine can help discard lightweight, moldy, and damaged kernels. Fields with ear rots should be harvested separately, and grain should be segregated to avoid mixing grain from contaminated fields with noncontaminated grain from other areas.

Postharvest. Moldy grain must be stored appropriately to minimize the impact on quality. Even a small amount of moldy grain can become a big problem with improper storage. For best results, grain that will be stored should be cooled to below 50°F (10°C) and dried immediately after harvest to below 15% moisture. Grain stored long term should be drier (below 13% moisture). Moldy grain should be stored separately from good-quality grain and checked periodically throughout the storage period to ensure that temperature and moisture levels remain constant. Moldy grain should be tested for mycotoxins prior to feeding animals.

#Diagnostic Key Words

late season, sandy soil, wounding, dry, warm, signs, ear mold

7.3 Cladosporium Ear Rot

Fungus: *Cladosporium herbarum*

Cladosporium ear rot is relatively uncommon, and economic losses have not been reported. No mycotoxins are associated with the fungus that causes this disease.

Symptoms and Signs

Cladosporium ear rot appears as a dark, greenish-black mold on kernels (Fig. 7.5). The discoloration usually forms first at the kernel base and then progresses upward. Symptoms are scattered across the ear, but the entire ear can eventually be colonized. In some cases, the seed coat will split to reveal clumps or tufts of dark mold growth. This ear rot can also develop as dark-green or brown, fuzzy growth that develops on and between the kernels (Fig. 7.6). Cladosporium ear rot is often observed with other ear rots.

Most Commonly Confused With

Aspergillus Ear Rot (7.2) • Penicillium Ear Rot (7.8) • Trichoderma Ear Rot (7.9)

The powdery mold produced by the fungus that causes Cladosporium ear rot looks very similar to the molds associated with several ear rots. Microscopic examination is necessary to distinguish among the fungi.

Favorable Conditions

Cladosporium ear rot is often associated with insect, hail, or frost damage. The development of disease is favored by wet weather during grain fill and by delayed harvest.

Management

Management is usually not needed for Cladosporium ear rot. A high level of moisture is required for the mold to grow; thus, using normal drying and storage procedures should prevent further growth in storage.

#Diagnostic Key Words

late season, wounding, wet, signs, ear mold, kernel discoloration

FIG. 7.5. Black mold on kernels produced by the fungus that causes Cladosporium ear rot.

FIG. 7.6. Fungal growth on kernels produced by the fungus that causes Cladosporium ear rot.

7.4 Diplodia Ear Rot

Fungi: *Stenocarpella maydis* and *Stenocarpella macrospora*

Diplodia ear rot can be caused by the same fungi that cause Diplodia stalk rot (section 6.4) and, to a lesser extent, Diplodia leaf streak (section 4.7). The importance of Diplodia ear rot in the United States and Canada has increased as conservation tillage practices have become more popular.

Symptoms and Signs

Symptoms of Diplodia ear rot begin on ears and are visible from R3 until R6. The husk of an infected ear and the associated ear leaf are often bleached while the rest of the plant stays green (Fig. 7.7). When the husk of a symptomatic ear is pulled back, a white mold is commonly observed on and especially between the kernels. The mold may first appear at the base of the ear (Fig. 7.8). Infected kernels eventually turn grayish-brown, and the entire ear may become rotted (Figs. 7.9 and 7.10). Infected kernels are lightweight and have reduced nutritional value.

The mold may also be apparent on the outside of the husk or on the shank. Often, the husk of the

FIG. 7.8. White mold at the base of the ear, a sign of Diplodia ear rot.

FIG. 7.7. Bleached husk, a symptom of Diplodia ear rot.

FIG. 7.9. Brown discoloration of the kernels, a symptom of Diplodia ear rot.

ear is difficult to remove and appears glued to the ear by the mold (see Fig. 7.10). A distinguishing characteristic of Diplodia ear rot is the appearance of very small, black, circular bodies embedded in the moldy husk or kernels or on the stalk. These are the pycnidia of the fungus, where new spores are produced (Fig. 7.11).

Diplodia ear rot will reduce yield and grain quality. The loss may worsen in grain, as the fungus

FIG. 7.10. Rotted ear and bleached husk, characteristics of Diplodia ear rot.

FIG. 7.11. Development of pycnidia on the kernels and cob, characteristic of the fungus that causes Diplodia ear rot.

continues to grow in storage and deteriorates grain quality. Diplodia ear rot is not known to produce harmful mycotoxins in the United States and Canada, but toxins associated with the ear rot have been reported in the Southern Hemisphere.

Most Commonly Confused With

Banded Leaf and Sheath Blight (4.2) • Gibberella Ear Rot (7.6)

Ears affected by Diplodia ear rot typically do not have the pinkish mold associated with Gibberella ear rot. Also, kernels infected with the fungus that causes Diplodia ear rot almost always appear with small, black pycnidia.

Favorable Conditions

Diplodia ear rot is favored by moderate, wet weather during grain fill. Planting corn following corn in the same field and planting hybrids with upward-oriented ears with tight husks also favor disease development. The ears are most susceptible during and right after silking.

The fungus overwinters as mycelium, spores, and pycnidia on corn residue and seed. Spores are spread primarily by splashing rain. The infection process for this disease is poorly understood, but symptoms first appear at the base of the ear. Corn-borer damage in the shank can provide an entry wound for the pathogen.

Although infection occurs at or after silking, the fungus can continue to spread on infected ears past R6 and until grain is below 18% moisture. Diplodia ear rot is more severe in years when wet conditions around silking are followed by a wet fall, which delays harvest and promotes fungal growth on the ears.

Management

Resistance. Resistance to ear rots varies among hybrids, although complete resistance is not available.

Cultural Practices. Inoculum levels can be reduced by rotating crops and reducing surface residue through tillage. If tillage is considered to decrease pathogen levels, efforts should be made to minimize soil erosion and maintain soil quality. In reduced-tillage systems, resistance and rotation are very important disease management practices.

Scouting. Fields should be scouted from R4 to the dent stage to identify areas in which Diplodia ear rot is problematic. At R4, it is often easier to observe affected plants because of the bleached leaves and husks associated with the infected ears. Fields with ear rots should be harvested before other fields to prevent further spread of mold on the ears.

Harvest. A properly adjusted combine can help discard lightweight, moldy, and damaged kernels.

Postharvest. Moldy grain must be stored appropriately to minimize the impact on grain quality. Even a small amount of moldy grain can become a big problem with improper storage. To reduce mold problems in storage, grain should be cooled to below 50°F (10°C) and dried immediately after harvest to below 18% moisture. Grain that will be stored long term should be drier (below 15% moisture). Moldy grain should be stored separately from good-quality grain and checked periodically throughout the storage period to ensure that temperature and moisture levels remain constant.

#Diagnostic Key Words

late season, wet, scattered, signs, ear mold, chaffy ears, husk/silk stuck

7.5 Fusarium Ear Rot and Fumonisin

Fungi: *Fusarium* species

Several fungi in the genus *Fusarium* cause Fusarium ear rot on corn, but *Fusarium verticillioides* is considered the primary pathogen in the United States and Canada, followed by *Fusarium proliferatum* and *Fusarium subglutinans*. Fusarium ear rot is found worldwide and is the most common ear disease on corn in the United States.

Fusarium species can produce the mycotoxins known as fumonisins. Fumonisins are acutely toxic to animals (especially pigs and horses) and have been linked to increased cancer rates and other human health problems. The U.S. Food and Drug Administration (FDA) has issued regulatory guidelines for safe levels of fumonisins in corn used for foods and animal feeds (available online at www.ngfa.org/wp-content/uploads/NGFAComplianceGuide-FDARegulatoryGuidanceforMycotoxins8-2011.pdf). In Canada, several government agencies provide inspection services and have issued regulations regarding mycotoxin limits. The Canadian Grain Commission regulates the grain-handling industry (www.grainscanada.gc.ca—select English or French tab), and the Canadian Food Inspection Agency regulates food safety, animal health, and plant health (www.inspection.gc.ca—select English or French tab). In addition, Health Canada has issued guidelines for allowable mycotoxin levels in food (available online at www.hc-sc.gc.ca/fn-an/securit/chem-chim/contaminants-guidelines-directives-eng.php).

Symptoms and Signs

Fusarium ear rot appears as a white to purple, cottony mold (Fig. 7.12); it can begin anywhere on the ear and is often associated with insect-damaged kernels. Usually, the entire ear does not rot, but affected kernels may be scattered or clustered throughout it (Fig. 7.13). Infected kernels are often tan or brown or have white streaks, which is described as a starburst pattern (Fig. 7.14). Infected kernels may also be symptomless.

Most Commonly Confused With

Gibberella Ear Rot (7.6)

The fungus that causes Gibberella ear rot typically produces a mat of pink-white mold, while the fungus that causes Fusarium ear rot produces a more white or purple mold that is scattered across the ear.

Favorable Conditions

Fusarium spores can be spread by wind and splashing rain to the silks or enter the plant tissue through kernels damaged by insects or hail. Insects act as vectors of *Fusarium* species, and consequently, Fusarium ear rot is usually more common in fields planted with non-Bt hybrids. The fungi also cause a stalk rot and can colonize any part of the corn plant. Some ear infections may result from the fungi entering the ear from the stalk. The fungi overwinter in corn residue and on dead, grassy weeds. However,

FIG. 7.12. White mold produced by the fungus that causes Fusarium ear rot.

FIG. 7.14. Starburst pattern on kernels associated with Fusarium ear rot.

FIG. 7.13. Rotted kernels scattered and clustered on ears, signs of Fusarium ear rot.

seed transmission does not play a large role in ear rot development.

Fusarium ear rot occurs under a wide range of weather conditions, but high temperatures (above 77°F [25°C]), drought stress before or after silking, and insect and mechanical damage favor infection and disease development. The optimum temperature for fumonisin production is 75°F (24°C). Although infection occurs at silking, the fungi can continue to spread on infected ears past R6 and until grain is below 18% moisture. Fusarium ear rot is more severe when weather conditions delay harvest and promote fungal growth on the ears.

Management

Resistance. Resistance to Fusarium ear rot varies among hybrids, but complete resistance is not available.

Cultural Practices. Crop rotation and tillage can reduce levels of inoculum in individual fields, but neither practice is typically effective in areas with intensive corn production because airborne spores are transported from neighboring fields. If tillage is considered to decrease pathogen levels, efforts should be made to minimize soil erosion and maintain soil quality. In reduced-tillage systems, resistance and rotation are very important disease management practices.

Insect Management. Managing insects using Bt proteins—particularly the European corn borer, corn earworm, and western bean cutworm—is an effective way of reducing Fusarium ear rot. The use of hybrid Bt traits is sometimes also associated with reductions in fumonisin contamination. Insecticide applications can also be effective if properly timed.

Scouting. Fields should be scouted at the dent stage to identify areas with mold problems. Once identified, these areas should be harvested as soon as possible to prevent further mold development. Fumonisin concentrations continue to increase in the field after physiological maturity of the crop; thus, early harvesting may help reduce the contamination level.

Harvest. A properly adjusted combine can help discard lightweight, moldy kernels and can also remove damaged kernels, which are more susceptible to mold development.

Postharvest. Moldy grain must be stored appropriately to minimize the impact on grain quality. Even a small amount of moldy grain can become a big problem with improper storage. For best results, grain that is to be stored should be cooled to below 50°F (10°C) and dried immediately after harvest to below 18% moisture. Grain that will be stored long term should be drier (below 15% moisture). Moldy grain should be stored separately from good-quality grain and checked periodically during storage to ensure that temperature and moisture levels remain constant.

#Diagnostic Key Words

late season, wounding, dry, warm, signs, ear mold, kernel discoloration

Gibberella Ear Rot and Mycotoxins

Fungus: *Fusarium graminearum*
(synonym: *Gibberella zeae*)

Gibberella ear rot is common throughout the U.S. Midwest and Northeast and in Ontario, Canada. This fungus also causes Gibberella stalk rot (section 6.6) on corn and Fusarium head blight on wheat and barley.

Symptoms and Signs

Gibberella ear rot can be identified by a red or pink mold that frequently develops at the tip of the ear and then grows down toward the shank (Fig. 7.15). The silks and husk may adhere to the ear because of the growth of excessive mold, which produces a fungal mat on the ear (Fig. 7.16). In severe cases, the pink mold is visible on the outside of the husk at the ear tip.

The causal fungus produces deoxynivalenol (also called DON and vomitoxin) and zearalenone, which are important mycotoxins in the northern U.S. Corn Belt and in Canada. Animals may refuse grain containing DON and regurgitate consumed food. Animals that consume zearalenone can experience infertility and abortion, along with other breeding issues.

Most Commonly Confused With

Diplodia Ear Rot (7.4) • Fusarium Ear Rot (7.5)

Sometimes, the pink coloration in the mold produced by the fungus that causes Gibberella ear

FIG. 7.16. Fungal mat on an ear produced by the fungus that causes Gibberella ear rot.

FIG. 7.15. Pink mold at the ear tips, a sign of Gibberella ear rot.

rot is very pale and appears white, making it highly similar to the mold produced by Diplodia ear rot (Fig. 7.17). However, kernels and ears affected by Diplodia ear rot often have small, black pycnidia visible in the inner cob tissue. Gibberella ear rot may also be confused with Fusarium ear rot, particularly if it is associated with hail-damaged kernels. Because of the risk of mycotoxin development, laboratory diagnosis may be needed to confirm the causal ear rot.

Favorable Conditions

Spores of the pathogen are spread by splashing rain and wind and infect the ear through the silks. The silks are most susceptible 2–6 days after emergence. Gibberella ear rot is favored by cool, wet weather after silking. The disease may be more prevalent in fields with infected corn or small-grain residue and in areas with extensive corn and small grain production. This ear rot may be higher in areas in which damage from insect feeding occurs, particularly those in which the western bean cutworm is prevalent. Although infection occurs at silking, the fungus can continue to spread on infected ears past R6 and until grain is below 18% moisture. Gibberella ear rot is more severe during years in which wet conditions occur around silking and a wet fall delays harvest, promoting fungal growth on the ear.

Management

Resistance. Resistance to Gibberella ear rot varies among hybrids, although complete resistance is not available. Hybrids with loose husks tend to be less likely to develop Gibberella ear rot but can be more prone to insect damage.

Cultural Practices. Inoculum levels can be reduced but not eliminated by rotating crops and reducing surface residue through tillage. If tillage is considered to decrease pathogen levels, efforts should be made to minimize soil erosion and maintain soil quality. In reduced-tillage systems, resistance and rotation are very important disease management practices.

Fungicides. Limited fungicides are currently labeled for use against this disease. Moreover, efficacy may vary based on disease progression, environmental conditions before and after application, spray coverage, active ingredient, and other factors.

Scouting. Fields should be scouted at the dent stage to identify areas with mold problems. Once identified, these areas should be harvested as soon as possible to prevent further mold and mycotoxin development.

Harvest. A properly adjusted combine can help discard lightweight, moldy kernels and can also remove damaged kernels, which are more susceptible to mold development.

Postharvest. Moldy grain must be stored appropriately to minimize the impact on grain quality. Even a small amount of moldy grain can become a big problem with improper storage. For best results, grain that will be stored on the farm should be cooled to below 50°F (10°C) and dried immediately after harvest to below 18% moisture. Grain that will be stored long term should be drier (below 15% moisture). Moldy grain should be stored separately from good quality grain and checked periodically throughout the storage period to ensure that temperature and moisture levels remain constant. Grain should be tested for mycotoxin levels before feeding it to susceptible animals.

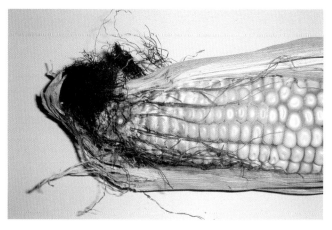

FIG. 7.17. Pale-whitish mold produced by the fungus that causes Gibberella ear rot.

#Diagnostic Key Words

late season, wet, cool, signs, ear mold, husk/silk stuck

7.7 Nigrospora Ear Rot

Fungus: *Nigrospora oryzae*

Nigrospora ear rot is not common but is sometimes associated with other ear rots. Stalk tissue may also be infected by the causal pathogen.

Symptoms and Signs

Nigrospora ear rot causes the kernels to be slightly bleached or streaked; they may also develop gray to black fungal growth and be peppered with masses of tiny, black spores (Figs. 7.18 and 7.19). These signs and symptoms occur mainly where the kernels attach to the cob, and infection is more severe at the base of the ear. Affected ears are lightweight and chaffy. Cob tissue (typically at the shank) shreds when ears are picked mechanically, which is a characteristic feature of the disease (Fig. 7.20). This ear rot is usually not apparent until harvest.

Most Commonly Confused With

Cladosporium Ear Rot (7.3) • Northern Corn Leaf Spot (race 1) (4.18)

Laboratory diagnosis is needed to distinguish between Nigrospora ear rot and Cladosporium ear rot.

Favorable Conditions

The pathogen is a weak parasitic fungus; thus, drought, frost, disease, and other stresses are required for infection to occur. Nigrospora ear rot is found occasionally in fields with low fertility levels and where corn has been prematurely killed. The fungus overwinters on corn residue and can be more prevalent when kernels have been damaged.

Management

Management is usually not needed for this disease.

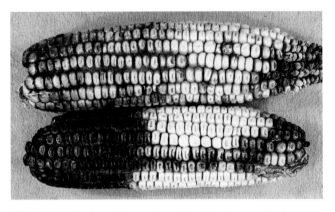

FIG. 7.18. Black mold produced by the fungus that causes Nigrospora ear rot.

#Diagnostic Key Words

late season, wounding, dry, signs, ear mold, kernel discoloration, chaffy ears

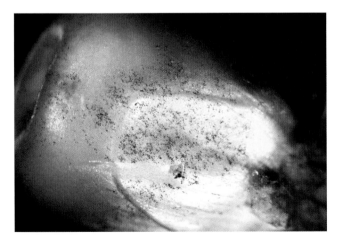

FIG. 7.19. Kernels peppered with spores of the fungus that causes Nigrospora ear rot.

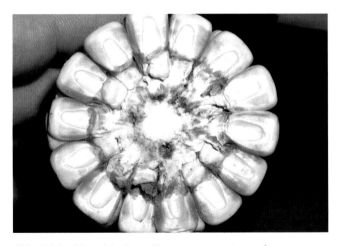

FIG. 7.20. Shredded ear tissue, a symptom of Nigrospora ear rot.

7.8 Penicillium Ear Rot

Fungi: *Penicillium* species

Penicillium ear rot occurs worldwide. It is caused by several species of *Penicillium,* some of which produce mycotoxins such as ochratoxins. These fungi can cause damage in the field and after harvest.

Symptoms and Signs

Penicillium ear rot is characterized by a green, blue-green, or denim-blue, powdery mold that develops between kernels, usually at the ear tip (Fig. 7.21). Infected kernels can appear bleached or streaked. In storage, an embryo discoloration known as blue-eye can occur (Fig. 7.22).

Most Commonly Confused With

Aspergillus Ear Rot (7.2) • **Cladosporium Ear Rot (7.3)** • **Trichoderma Ear Rot (7.9)**

Mold color can help distinguish among ear rots, but because these colors can be difficult to distinguish in the field, microscopic examination may be necessary for definitive identification. Blue-eye kernels in storage are also often infected with an *Aspergillus* species.

Favorable Conditions

The *Penicillium* species that cause this ear rot overwinter in the soil and on other host plants. Inoculum is spread by wind and rain, and disease occurs when the ears are exposed to extended wet conditions. Penicillium ear rot occurs primarily on ears damaged mechanically, by hail, or by insects (Fig. 7.23). In storage, Penicillium ear rot can be more prevalent when kernel moisture is greater than 18%.

Management

Management is usually not needed for this disease. If the level of disease is severe, the grain should be tested for ochratoxins.

FIG. 7.22. Blue-eye in stored grain caused by infection with a *Penicillium* species.

FIG. 7.21. Mold at the ear tip produced by the fungus that causes Penicillium ear rot.

FIG. 7.23. Penicillium ear rot associated with hail damage.

Postharvest. Measures should be taken to dry grain to a safe level before storage. If blue-eye is observed in stored grain, the grain should be tested for mycotoxins (aflatoxin and ochratoxins) before it is fed to animals.

Diagnostic Key Words

late season, wounding, wet, signs, ear mold, kernel discoloration

Fungus: *Trichoderma viride*

Trichoderma ear rot is observed occasionally across the United States and Canada but is not typically severe.

Symptoms and Signs

Trichoderma ear rot appears as a dark-green to dark-blue mold that grows on or between the kernels and husk (Figs. 7.24 and 7.25). Often, this mold

FIG. 7.24. Mold growing on and between kernels, a sign of Trichoderma ear rot.

FIG. 7.25. Green mold on kernels produced by the fungus that causes Trichoderma ear rot.

covers the whole ear. In severe cases, the kernels may germinate or sprout while still on the cob (Fig. 7.26). This ear rot does not typically produce economic losses, except when husk integrity has been severely compromised. No associated mycotoxin issues have been reported.

Most Commonly Confused With

Aspergillus Ear Rot (7.2) · Cladosporium Ear Rot (7.3) · Penicillium Ear Rot (7.8)

The color of the causal fungus is usually more of an intense green or turquoise than the colors of other ear rot fungi. Mold color can help distinguish among ear rots, but because these colors can be difficult to distinguish in the field, microscopic examination may be necessary for definitive identification.

Favorable Conditions

Trichoderma species overwinter in soil and on plant debris. Trichoderma ear rot often occurs when ears are exposed to extended wet conditions. Mechanical and insect injury and damage caused by birds to developing ears also provide points at which the pathogen can enter the husk.

Management

Management is usually not needed for this disease.

Postharvest. The mold produced by the causal fungus requires a high level of moisture to grow. Normal drying and storage procedures should stop further growth in storage.

FIG. 7.26. Kernel sprouting in the husk, a common result of Trichoderma ear rot.

#Diagnostic Key Words

late season, wounding, scattered, signs, ear mold

Noninfectious Disorders

8.1 Nutrient and Fertilizer Disorders

8.2 Chemical Injury

8.3 Environmental Conditions and Genetic Disorders

8.4 Insect Injury

Plant injuries can be caused by many types of noninfectious agents, such as nutrients and fertilizers, herbicides, environmental conditions, and genetic disorders. Insects can also injure corn plants as they feed. These injuries can sometimes be confused with those caused by infectious plant pathogens, because the symptoms and signs may be similar. It is important to determine the differences between look-alike disorders and diseases when selecting management strategies. For example, applying a fungicide will not be effective at reducing symptoms caused by a nutrient deficiency, environmental injury, or bacterial disease. Acting on an improper diagnosis wastes time and money, so distinguishing between symptoms and signs of diseases and disorders is important.

8.1 Nutrient and Fertilizer Disorders

Nutrient imbalances can interfere with the proper development of corn plants. Plants with nutrient deficiencies may be more susceptible to certain diseases or mistakenly identified as being diseased. In many cases, nutrient disorders are tied to soil properties (such as pH and soil texture) and environmental conditions (such as cold soils, cloudy days, dry soils, and so on). Fertilizer injuries can also produce symptoms similar to those of certain diseases.

Many of the disorders caused by nutrients and fertilizers resemble corn diseases such as anthracnose leaf blight (section 4.1) and gray leaf spot (section 4.10), as well as virus diseases (sections 4.14–4.16 and 4.24) and diseases caused by nematodes (sections 5.5–5.7). Many nutrient disorders also produce similar signs and symptoms, and proper diagnosis requires submitting plant and soil samples to a laboratory for diagnosis.

The following sections describe common nutrient and fertilizer disorders in corn.

Magnesium Deficiency

Symptoms first appear on the lower leaves. The outer edges of the leaves are striped yellow or white. Beading, or the development of small areas of dead tissue within the stripes, may also occur. Purpling may occur on the older leaves (Fig. 8.1).

Diagnostic Key Words

early season, midseason, late season, leaf discoloration

Nitrogen Deficiency

Symptoms first appear on the lower leaves (Fig. 8.2). The leaves yellow from tip to base in a V-shaped pattern. Nitrogen deficiency can be confused with anthracnose leaf blight (section 4.1), Goss's wilt (section 4.9), and Stewart's disease (section 4.23).

Diagnostic Key Words

early season, midseason, late season, leaf discoloration

Potassium Deficiency

The lower leaves yellow from the margins inward, and the leaf edges turn brown (Fig. 8.3).

Diagnostic Key Words

midseason, late season, leaf discoloration, leaf margins dead, chaffy ears

Sulfur Deficiency

The tissue between the leaf veins becomes light green or yellow, giving the leaves a striped appearance (Fig. 8.4).

Diagnostic Key Words

early season, midseason, late season, leaf discoloration

Zinc Deficiency

Yellow stripes usually appear on the upper leaves. The stripes are usually wider than those associated with sulfur deficiency, and they start from the midvein of the leaf (Fig. 8.5).

Diagnostic Key Words

early season, leaf discoloration

FIG. 8.1. Purpling along the edges of leaves, symptomatic of magnesium deficiency.

FIG. 8.4. Sulfur deficiency can make plants appear yellow (right).

FIG. 8.2. Nitrogen-deficient corn, characterized by yellowing of the lower leaves.

FIG. 8.5. Zinc-deficient corn, displaying wide, yellow stripes on the upper leaves.

FIG. 8.3. Foliar symptoms of potassium deficiency.

Fertilizer Injury

Applying a pop-up fertilizer can injure a germinating seedling and stunt or kill a plant. Symptoms may be observed on the roots of young seedlings, appearing as reduced or discolored roots, prolific root branching, or death.

A side-dress application of nitrogen can also burn plant tissue if the solution comes into contact with the leaves. Older leaves will develop spots, but younger leaves will not be affected (Fig. 8.6).

#Diagnostic Key Words

early season, poor emergence, leaf discoloration, leaf margins dead

FIG. 8.6. Foliar symptoms of fertilizer injury.

Herbicides and crop additives are among the types of chemicals that can injure corn plants. Both can cause injuries that may be confused with disease symptoms.

Herbicide Injury

Paraquat is a commonly used herbicide that causes injury mimicking plant disease on corn, including leaf spots and blighting of affected leaves (Fig. 8.7). Holcus leaf spot (section 4.12) is an example of a foliar disease that can be difficult to distinguish from paraquat injury. Herbicides can also cause stippling and a type of leaf distortion known as buggy-whipping, both of which resemble symptoms of crazy top (section 4.6) and virus diseases (sections 4.14–4.16 and 4.24). (See also "Buggy-Whipping/Plant Distortion" at the end of section 8.3.) Residual herbicides and early postemergence herbicide applications can cause symptoms that resemble those of seedling blight diseases (sections 5.1 and 5.2) (Fig. 8.8). Nematode injury to the roots may also resemble herbicide injury (sections 5.5–5.7). Herbicide injury may create conditions that favor the development of certain diseases, including common smut (section 4.4) and Rhizoctonia crown and brace root rot (5.4).

To distinguish herbicide injury from disease, it is necessary to find out whether the field in question or a field nearby was treated with an herbicide prior to the appearance of symptoms. If it was, the product or products used, application rate, application timing, and field history (previous crop grown) should all be determined to help make a proper diagnosis.

It is also important to note the pattern of symptom expression in the affected field. If herbicide drift is suspected, symptoms in the field should become successively less severe from the edge of the field moving inward. That is, the highest density of symptomatic plants should be observed closest to the target site (the field with the herbicide application), and symptoms should decline in incidence and severity when moving away from the target site. In addition, the pattern of symptoms should follow the same direction as the prevailing winds on the day the herbicide was applied.

If symptoms do not follow a gradient pattern across the field and plants surrounding the field are not affected, then the symptoms may be caused by disease. Plants with disease typically occur randomly throughout the field or in scattered patches, and severity may vary across the field and from plant to plant.

Diagnosis of an herbicide injury typically requires submitting plant samples to a diagnostic laboratory and examining herbicide application records for the damaged field and possibly surrounding fields.

#Diagnostic Key Words

early season, midseason, late season, poor emergence, distortion, lesions, leaf discoloration

FIG. 8.7. Tan spots caused by paraquat injury.

FIG. 8.8. Injury caused by the herbicide clethodim.

Crop Additive Injury

Nonionic surfactants and crop oils are commonly added to pesticides (such as fungicides) to improve their efficacy. These additives can cause phytotoxicity, resulting in foliar spotting or stippling that resembles symptoms of disease. Additionally, if any of these products is applied prior to tasseling, it can cause ear injury, leading to arrested ear symptoms or other ear deformities (Fig. 8.9).

#Diagnostic Key Words

early season, midseason, late season, abnormal ears, leaf discoloration

FIG. 8.9. Arrested ear development caused by application of a nonionic surfactant.

8.3 Environmental Conditions and Genetic Disorders

A variety of environmental conditions can affect corn growth and development. When conditions are not ideal for growth, plants may show evidence of stress, which can resemble symptoms of disease or make plants more susceptible to disease. Corn may also exhibit disease-like symptoms that are caused by the genetics of the plant.

The following sections describe common environmental conditions and genetic-related issues that cause disorders mimicking diseases.

Soil Crusting

A hard crust may develop on the soil surface when certain conditions occur during and after planting and thus prevent seedling emergence. Seedlings may appear bent or twisted or even die (Fig. 8.10). The symptoms on seedlings and the loss of plant stand can be confused with the effects of seedling diseases (sections 5.1, 5.2, and 5.4).

#Diagnostic Key Words

early season, fieldwide, poor emergence

FIG. 8.10. Emerging seedling is bent because of soil crusting.

Frost Damage

Plant injury can occur when temperatures drop to 29°F (–1.5°C) or below. The water-soaked, wilted tissue caused by frost damage can resemble the symptoms of Pythium seedling blight and root rot (section 5.2) (Fig. 8.11). Plant growth should resume as long as the growing point is not damaged and good weather follows the frost event.

#Diagnostic Key Words

early season, late season, fieldwide, poor emergence, chaffy ears (late season)

FIG. 8.11. Water-soaked and wilted tissue caused by frost damage.

Lesion Mimic/Physiological Leaf Spots and Stripes/Genetic Flecking

The disorder referred to as lesion mimic, physiological leaf spots and stripes, and genetic flecking is caused by plant genetics and can produce the spotting and streaking symptoms characteristic of various leaf diseases (Fig. 8.12), such as eyespot (section 4.8), holcus leaf spot (section 4.12), Physoderma brown spot and stalk rot (section 4.19), and virus diseases (sections 4.14–4.16 and 4.24). Symptoms often occur on single plants across a field or a group of plants in a field. Usually, every leaf on the affected plant will show symptoms. The stripe symptoms caused by viruses occur from the point of infection up the plant.

#Diagnostic Key Words

early season, midseason, late season, patchy, scattered, leaf discoloration

FIG. 8.12. Symptoms of lesion mimic vary and may include **(A)** streaks and **(B and C)** spots on leaves.

Purple Leaf Sheath/Pollen Rot/ Purple Sheath Blight

Purple leaf sheath (also known as pollen rot and purple sheaf blight) is more prevalent during growing seasons with high humidity. Dark-purple blotches develop on the leaf sheaths of plants, primarily after R2 (Fig. 8.13). These symptoms are caused by saprophytes feeding on pollen and other materials that have been deposited between the leaf sheath and the stalk. Symptoms can resemble those of banded leaf and sheath blight (section 4.2) and Physoderma brown spot (section 4.19) when they develop on the sheath.

#Diagnostic Key Words

midseason, late season, leaf discoloration

Flooding

Extended flooding can cause plants to turn yellow, wilt, and die (Fig. 8.14). Flooding before V6 may have the greatest impact on yield. Seed decay, Pythium seedling blight and root rot (section 5.2), and crazy top (section 4.6) are all more likely to occur in flooded fields. Plant injury from prolonged exposure to flooding can resemble symptoms of seedling blight.

#Diagnostic Key Words

early season, midseason, late season, wet, ponding/wet soils, poor emergence, death, leaf margins dead

Drought

When conditions are too dry, the leaves roll and can turn grayish (Fig. 8.15A). In addition, plant growth is reduced, and plants can even die prematurely. Drought stress during the reproductive stages causes the most injury, resulting in poor pollination, kernel weight reduction, kernel abortion, and other symptoms (Fig. 8.15B). Drought-stressed plants may also be more susceptible to stalk rots and lodging (Chapter 6), and a lack of moisture can induce nitrogen deficiency (section 8.1), even if the nutrient

is present in a sufficient amount in the soil. Leaf scorching and early leaf death can occur, as well.

Drought-stressed plants sometimes exhibit symptoms resembling those of Goss's wilt (leaf blight phase) (section 4.9), Stewart's disease (section 4.23), and diseases caused by nematodes (sections 5.5–5.7).

#Diagnostic Key Words

early season, midseason, late season, dry, sandy soils, wilting, death, abnormal ears, chaffy ears, leaf margins dead

FIG. 8.13. Blotches caused by purple leaf sheath.

FIG. 8.14. Damage caused by flooding.

Hail Damage

Depending on the severity of the hail storm, damage can include defoliation, reduced stands, twisted whorls, and injured stalks and ears (Fig. 8.16). The yield loss that results will depend on the severity of the damage and the growth stage of the plants when the damage occurs. The greatest yield loss will occur with corn that is tasseling, and the least yield loss will occur with corn injured prior to V6.

The damage caused by hail is usually not confused with the symptoms of disease. However, the wounds caused by hail damage favor the development of common smut (section 4.4), Goss's wilt (section 4.9), and stalk and ear rots (Chapters 6 and 7, respectively). Injury to ears can also increase the risk for mycotoxin development in grain.

#Diagnostic Key Words

early season, midseason, late season, fieldwide, chaffy ears (R4–R5 event)

FIG. 8.15. A, Drought-stressed plants. **B,** Effects of drought stress on an ear.

High Temperatures

High temperatures can cause leaf scorch, which may resemble the symptoms of several foliar diseases, including Goss's wilt (section 4.9), northern corn leaf blight (section 4.17), and Stewart's disease (section 4.23) (Fig. 8.17). Typically, high temperatures result in higher transpiration rates, and when combined with drought stress, they can severely reduce kernel weight and size and increase maturation rate during the reproductive stages.

#Diagnostic Key Words

midseason, late season, warm, leaf margins dead

FIG. 8.16. Hail damage.

FIG. 8.17. Leaf scorch.

Stalk Lodging

The term lodging can be defined as the leaning of stalks to near ground level toward the end of the growing season (Fig. 8.18). It can result from development of a stalk rot (Chapter 6) and may cause harvest difficulties. Severe foliar diseases (Chapter 4) and other stresses can predispose plants to stalk rot and subsequent lodging.

#Diagnostic Key Words

late season, lodging

FIG. 8.18. Stalk lodging.

Greensnap

The disorder known as greensnap occurs when the stalk breaks off at a node (Fig. 8.19). Typically, this is caused by high winds prior to the plant's tasseling in the late vegetative stages. The yield reduction associated with greensnap is determined by the point at which the stalk breaks and the growth stage of the plant.

This disorder may be confused with Physoderma stalk rot (section 4.19).

#Diagnostic Key Words

early season, midseason, wounding

FIG. 8.19. Greensnap.

Lightning Damage

A circular patch of dead plants that has clearly defined edges may indicate a lightning strike (Fig. 8.20). Most if not all the plants in the center of such a spot are killed, and plants toward the edges of the patch are less severely affected. A circular area of lightning-damaged plants may be 30-plus feet (9-plus m) in diameter.

Lightning damage may be confused with diseases that occur in patches, such as seedling blight (sections 5.1, 5.2, and 5.4). However, patches caused by disease develop differently from those caused by lightning, which appear suddenly and have clearly defined edges.

#Diagnostic Key Words

early season, midseason, late season, patchy, wounding, death

FIG. 8.20. Lightning damage.

Buggy-Whipping/Plant Distortion

As the leaves emerge, they may become trapped in the whorl and twist the upper part of the plant and fail to unfurl (Fig. 8.21). Leaves typically unfurl within a week or two and will be very yellow and appear crinkled. Some hybrids are more prone to buggy-whipping than others. Also, hail damage, herbicide injury, and rapid growth at stage V6 are all factors associated with buggy-whipping. Yield is not affected by this disorder unless the leaves never unfurl.

#Diagnostic Key Words

early season, scattered, wounding, distortion

FIG. 8.21. Buggy-whipping.

8.4 Insect Injury

Many insects and insectlike animals obtain their energy from feeding on corn. Insect and mite pests consume the leaves, roots, tassels, ears, and silks or withdraw fluids from corn plants. Thus, these pests may directly destroy plant tissue or reduce the amount of water and nutrients available for plant functions. Feeding can weaken the plant, interrupt pollination, cause lodging and distortion such as goose-necking, and create entry points for pathogens.

Certain insect activity can be conducive to disease development. Many diseases are favored by the presence of insects, including the following:

Common smut (section 4.4)

Corn stunt (4.5)

Maize bushy stunt (4.13)

Maize chlorotic dwarf (4.14)

Maize chlorotic mottle (4.15)

Maize dwarf mosaic (4.16)

Stewart's disease (4.23)

Other viruses (4.24)

Anthracnose stalk rot (6.1)

Aspergillus ear rot (7.2)

Cladosporium ear rot (7.3)

Diplodia ear rot (7.4)

Fusarium ear rot (7.5)

Gibberella ear rot (7.6)

Penicillium ear rot (7.8)

Trichoderma ear rot (7.9)

Also, non-Bt corn may be vulnerable to greater insect injury, leading to increased development of ear rots (Chapter 7).

Visible symptoms of insect injury can sometimes resemble symptoms caused by diseases such as eyespot (section 4.8), Goss's wilt (section 4.9), seedling blight (sections 5.1, 5.2, and 5.4), stalk rots (Chapter 6), and virus diseases (sections 4.14–4.16 and 4.24). Proper diagnosis may require submitting plant samples to a laboratory. Before implementing a management plan, it is important to determine if the observed symptoms are caused by an insect, a pathogen, or both.

Insects That Damage Seeds/Seedlings

Insects that feed on seeds/seedlings can cause corn plants to die before or shortly after emergence, and the suspected cause may be severe Pythium seedling blight and root rot (section 5.2). Farmers should check belowground for evidence of insect damage to seeds/seedlings or for the insects themselves. Insects that can cause damage to seedlings include the stalk borer, wireworms, grubs, the seedcorn maggot, and seedcorn beetles, among others (Figs. 8.22 and 8.23). Wireworm injury to corn roots can be confused with that caused by certain nematodes (sections 5.5–5.7).

Insectlike animals, which are often tiny, can also be falsely suspected of causing seed/seedling death. These tiny animals feed on the dead and decaying tissues produced by diseases and insects. Examples of these scavengers include millipedes, potworms (earthworm-like), mites, and springtails.

#Diagnostic Key Words

early season, wounding, poor emergence

FIG. 8.22. Wireworm and feeding damage.

Insects and Slugs That Feed on Leaves

Multiple insects and slugs feed on the green epidermal layer of the corn leaf, causing damage ranging from tiny scars to a parchment-like appearance. This damage may be confused with many fungal disease lesions and leaf blights, depending on the severity. The list of causal organisms includes slugs, the corn rootworm beetle, the corn flea beetle, the cereal leaf beetle larvae, the Japanese beetle, and the woolly bear caterpillar, among others (Figs. 8.24, 8.25, 8.26, 8.27, 8.28).

#Diagnostic Key Words

wounding, early season, midseason, late season, leaf discoloration

FIG. 8.23. Grub and feeding damage.

FIG. 8.24. Corn slug feeding damage.

FIG. 8.25. Corn rootworm feeding damage.

FIG. 8.26. Corn flea beetle and feeding scar.

FIG. 8.27. Japanese beetles and feeding damage.

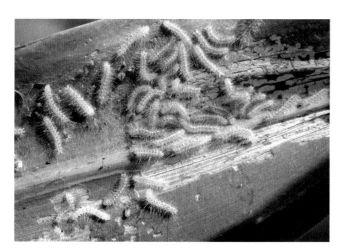

FIG. 8.28. Caterpillars and feeding damage.

Insects and Mites Whose Activity Can Resemble Disease

Corn Blotch Leafminer

Damage caused by the corn blotch leafminer can resemble symptoms of foliar diseases such as Goss's wilt (section 4.9), gray leaf spot (section 4.10), northern corn leaf blight (section 4.17), and Stewart's disease (section 4.23). The feeding of larvae creates white, transparent streaks or blotches on the leaf, which expand as the larvae tunnel within it (Fig. 8.29).

#Diagnostic Key Words

midseason, late season, leaf discoloration

FIG. 8.29. Corn blotch leafminer feeding damage.

Spider Mites and Thrips

Feeding from spider mites and thrips can cause damage that resembles the symptoms of virus diseases (sections 4.14–4.16 and 4.24). Feeding produces tiny, white to yellowish spots or scratches; they start from the midrib and are more prevalent on the underside of the leaf, giving it a speckled appearance (Fig. 8.30).

FIG. 8.30. Spider mite feeding damage, ranging from slight (top) to severe (bottom).

#Diagnostic Key Words

early season, midseason, late season, leaf discoloration

Other Conditions Caused by Insects

Other insects can cause tillering (billbug), lodging (corn rootworm), and abnormal ear development (stink bugs, grasshoppers, caterpillars) during their various life processes.

#Diagnostic Key Words

wounding, early season, midseason, late season, tillering, lodging, abnormal ears

Diseases of Worldwide Importance That Do Not Occur in the United States and Canada

9.1 Fijiviruses

Maize rough dwarf (*Maize rough dwarf virus* [MRDV]), maize rio cuarto (*Mal de rio cuarto virus* [MRCV]), and rice black-streaked dwarf (*Rice black-streaked dwarf virus* [RBSDV]) are corn diseases caused by fijiviruses. These pathogens are only slightly different from one another and are all spread by planthoppers. Fijiviruses have been observed in Europe, Asia, South America, and Africa (most recently).

Symptoms of these virus diseases include the development of galls on leaf veins (enations) and other tissues, formation of chlorotic stripes, stunting caused by the shortened lengths of internodes, sterility, leaf distortion, leaf darkening, and discoloration and size reduction of root systems (Fig. 9.1). Resistant cultivars can be used for disease management.

#Diagnostic Key Words

galls, stunting, distortion, leaf discoloration

FIG. 9.1. Field affected by a fijivirus.

9.2 Maize Streak

Maize streak, which is caused by *Maize streak virus* (MSV), is an important disease in Africa and also infects corn in Southeast Asia. The pathogen is transmitted by leafhoppers and has many crop plant hosts in addition to corn.

Symptoms include the formation of chlorotic spots on leaves, which can coalesce into streaks (Fig. 9.2), along with stunting and ultimately yield loss (Fig. 9.3). Resistant cultivars can be used for disease management.

#Diagnostic Key Words

stunting, leaf discoloration

FIG. 9.2. Chlorotic streaks on leaves, a symptom of maize streak.

FIG. 9.3. Stunted plant growth, a symptom of maize streak.

9.3 Late Wilt

Late wilt (also known as black bundle disease) is caused by the fungus *Harpophora maydis* (synonym *Cephalosporium maydis*). This disease was first described in Egypt around 1965 but has since spread to other parts of Africa, as well as to Asia and western Europe. The spread of late wilt has caused concern about its potential to become established in North America and South America.

Symptoms of this vascular disease include leaf wilting, formation of basal internode streaks, stalk withering, discoloration of the pith and vascular tissues, and premature plant death (Figs. 9.4 and 9.5).

#Diagnostic Key Words

wilting, rotting stalk interior, death

FIG. 9.4. Discoloration of pith, symptomatic of late wilt.

FIG. 9.5. Premature plant death caused by late wilt.

9.4 Asian Downy Mildews

FIG. 9.6. Symptoms of Philippine downy mildew, one of the Asian downy mildews: **(A)** leaves with chlorotic/necrotic streaks and shredding and **(B)** stunted growth.

Several downy mildew pathogens can infect corn and cause various diseases, including *Peronosclerospora maydis* (Java downy mildew), *Peronosclerospora philippinensis* (Philippine downy mildew), *Peronosclerospora sacchari* (sugarcane downy mildew), and *Sclerophthora rayssiae* var. *zeae* (brown stripe downy mildew). In tropical regions of Asia, these diseases can cause severe damage to corn.

Symptoms include chlorotic and/or necrotic streaks on leaves, leaf lesions, leaf shredding, stunting, lodging, sterility, tillering, tissue distortion, and death (Fig. 9.6). Leaf streaks may exhibit fungal growth. Systemic infection may eventually occur.

#Diagnostic Key Words

leaf discoloration, stunting, tillering, distortion, death

CHAPTER 10

A Closer Look

Many diseases have symptoms and signs that are difficult to diagnose, especially with the naked eye. To ensure accurate diagnosis, plant samples can be sent to a local plant-diagnostic clinic, where specialized methods and equipment are used to determine the cause of disease. In some cases, however, all that is needed to accurately diagnose a disease is a hand lens, a magnification application (or app), or a simple microscope. It is also possible to use a moist chamber to induce certain disease-causing organisms to form structures that can help in identification.

USING A HAND LENS

Most people do not have access to a microscope, but a hand lens (similar to a magnifying glass) is likely available. A hand lens can easily be carried into the field and provides one of the simplest ways to take a closer look at a problem.

Follow these basic guidelines to use a hand lens successfully:

1. Identify your dominant eye (Fig. 10.1A).
    a. Hold your hands in front of you, and make a triangle with your thumbs and pointer fingers.
    b. With both eyes, look through the triangle and focus on an object far in front of you.
    c. Pull your hands toward your face until they are touching it.
    d. The eye your hands move toward is your dominant eye.
2. Hold the hand lens close to your dominant eye and close to the object you are looking at. Do not hold the lens at arm's length (Fig. 10.1B).

3. Move the lens and/or the object to get things into focus. The greater the magnification of the lens, the closer the object will need to be to the lens to be in focus. For example, if you are using a 10× lens, the focal point will be about 1 inch (2.50 cm) from the lens. If you are using a 20× lens, the focal point will be about ½ inch (1.25 cm) from the lens.

FIG. 10.1. A, Before using a hand lens in the field, identify your dominant eye. **B,** Hold the lens close to your dominant eye and the object you are looking at (not away from your eye, as shown here).

4. Getting the right light is important. You may need to position yourself so that your shadow is not in the way. Sometimes, removing your hat will be helpful.

LOOKING AT MICROSCOPIC IMAGES

Microscopes are now simple and mobile enough to be used in the field, and they can even be attached to mobile devices (Fig. 10.2A). Several inexpensive microscope cameras are also available that can be plugged into a computer. Be sure to refer to the owner's manual for your microscope for instructions on how to maximize its viewing capabilities (Fig. 10.2B).

Looking at microscopic images opens up another world of identification possibilities. This will become evident after you glance at a leaf sample and observe the diverse characteristics of the microorganisms it contains. The following set of microscopic images of common disease pathogens will be useful in confirming diagnoses in corn:

- Anthracnose: Acervuli (fruiting structures) of the causal fungus with spinelike setae (Fig. 10.3)
- Northern corn leaf blight (NCLB): Spores of the causal fungus (Fig. 10.4)

FIG. 10.3. Anthracnose acervuli with setae.

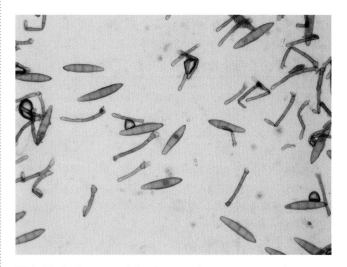

FIG. 10.4. Spores of the fungus that causes northern corn leaf blight.

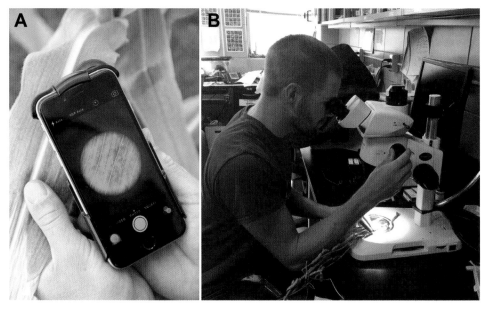

FIG. 10.2. A, Mobile microscope attachment being used in the field. **B**, Dissecting microscope being used in the laboratory.

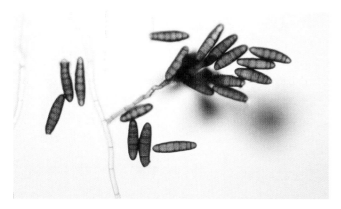

FIG. 10.5. Spores of the fungus that causes northern corn leaf spot.

- Northern corn leaf spot (NCLS): Spores of the causal fungus (Fig. 10.5)
- Southern rust: Spores of the causal fungus (Fig. 10.6)
- Southern corn leaf blight (SCLB): Spores of the causal fungus (Fig. 10.7)

Common views that are not pathogens (but can be confused with pathogens) include leaf trichomes (Fig. 10.8).

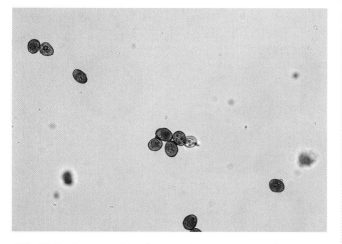

FIG. 10.6. Spores of the fungus that causes southern rust.

FIG. 10.8. Leaf trichomes.

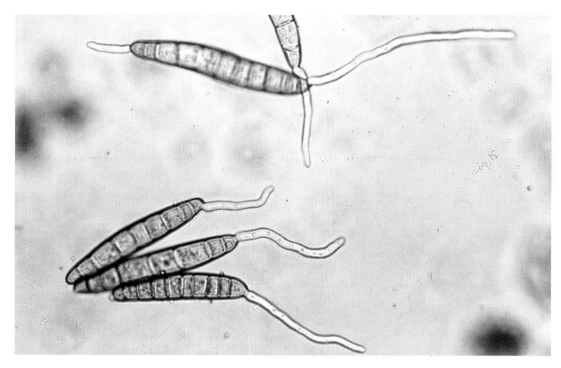

FIG. 10.7. Spores of the fungus that causes southern corn leaf blight.

Hand lenses and most mobile microscopes are not powerful enough to see bacteria streaming or oozing from leaves, which can be sign of a bacterial disease. However, if you have access to a powerful microscope and sample preparation equipment, you can attempt to view the streaming by following these steps:

1. Cut a small section of the symptomatic tissue, and place it on a glass slide (Fig. 10.9A). Be sure to cut a portion of the leaf that includes both the lesion and healthy leaf tissue. Doing so will ensure that the plant sample is from the edge of the lesion.
2. Place water on the leaf section (usually, only a few drops) and cover with a coverslip (Figs. 10.9B and C).

3. Look for bacteria oozing from the diseased section into the surrounding water (Fig. 10.9D). (*Note*: Bacterial streaming may be confused with plant sap moving. If you observe streaming, send a sample to a plant-diagnostic lab for final confirmation.)

CREATING A MOIST CHAMBER

A homemade moist chamber can be used to induce certain fungal pathogens to produce fruiting bodies and spores on plant tissue, which can aid in their identification. Using a moist chamber can therefore help you confirm what you suspect is the disease. However, if you are uncertain of what you are looking for, viewing samples that have been

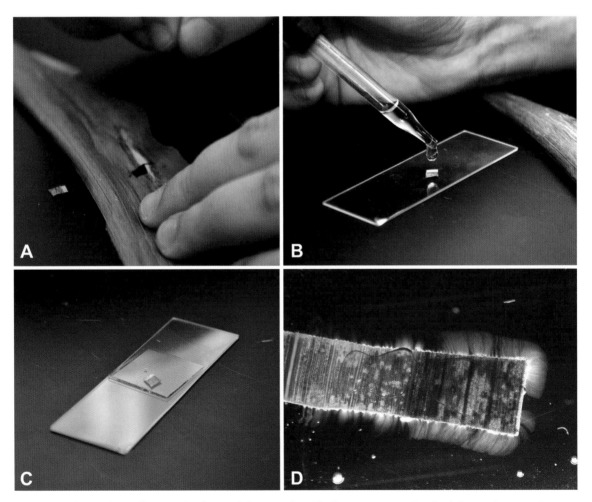

FIG. 10.9. Procedures for viewing bacterial streaming: **A,** Cut symptomatic plant tissue to mount on a slide. **B,** Place the plant tissue on the slide and then add water. **C,** Place a coverslip over the plant tissue. **D,** Watch for bacteria streaming out of the plant tissue.

incubated in a moist chamber can be frustrating, because you will see many types of spores and have limited guides to help identify them. (Many fungi will grow inside the moist chamber, not just the plant pathogens.)

To incubate a plant sample in a moist chamber, follow these steps:

1. Collect plant material that displays moderate disease symptoms (foliar lesions). If the material is too diseased or if the lesions are very old, the chance of other microorganisms (saprophytes) growing will be great, making it difficult to identify the original pathogen.
2. Place the plant material in a moist chamber (Fig. 10.10A). Types of moist chambers range from a temperature-controlled chamber that regulates the moisture in the air to a sealed plastic bag, plastic food storage container, or glass canning jar with a moist paper towel inside it.
3. If possible, clean the surface of the plant material with 70% isopropanol or 0.1–1.0% sodium hypochlorite (bleach) to reduce the growth of nondisease-causing organisms (saprophytes) on the material before placing it in the chamber (Fig. 10.10B). Let the disinfectant evaporate.
4. Store the sample at a moderate temperature (approximately 70°F [21°C]) for 18–24 hours. Make sure the container is closed tightly, and keep the sample out of direct sunlight.
5. Remove the sample and check for fungal growth on the lesion (Fig. 10.11).

FIG. 10.10. **A**, Example of a moist chamber. **B**, The sample should be cleaned before it is placed in the moist chamber to prevent the growth of nonpathogenic organisms.

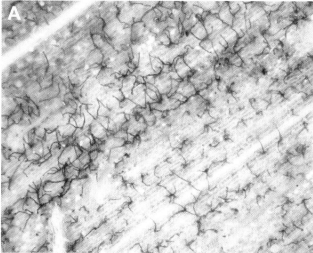

FIG. 10.11. Fungal growth on the lesion: **A**, Spores of the fungus that causes northern corn leaf blight. **B**, Pustules of the fungus that causes southern corn rust.

Abbreviations: adj. = adjective; pl. = plural; v. = verb

acervulus (pl. acervuli): a fruiting structure of some fungi in which conidia are formed; shaped like a cushion.

alternate host: one of the two species of plants required for some fungal pathogens to complete their life cycles.

alternative host: a plant other than the main host that can be colonized by a parasitic pathogen (but is not required for the pathogen to complete its life cycle).

aphid: a small, plant-feeding insect capable of spreading plant disease.

apothecium (pl. apothecia): a spore-producing, mushroomlike fungal structure; shaped like a saucer.

basal: located at the base—for example, the base of a stem.

cellulose: the substance composing the cell walls of plants.

chasmothecium (pl. chasmothecia): the fruiting body that contain spores of the powdery mildew pathogens.

chlorosis (adj. chlorotic): the yellowing of plant tissue caused by the destruction of chlorophyll; a common disease symptom.

conidium (pl. conidia): a fungal spore usually produced at the tip or side of a hypha.

cytoplasm: the cell contents surrounding the nucleus and containing some of the plant genes.

epidermis: the surface layer of plant tissue.

exudate: the fluid emitted from an organism through pores or a wound.

f. sp.: abbreviation for "*forma specialis*" (Latin for "special form"); can be used following a scientific name to designate a form that is adapted to a specific host.

foliage: plant leaves.

germination: the initial growth of a plant or pathogen from a seed or spore.

girdling: occurs when a lesion or growth surrounds or encircles the plant stem or root.

graminaceous: of, relating to, or denoting plants of the grass family.

hypha (pl. hyphae): a threadlike strand of fungal mycelium that extracts nutrients and water from the host.

inbred line: a genetically stable line that is developed by transferring pollen from an individual corn plant to the silks of the same plant for several generations; inbred lines as parents in hybrid production.

inoculum (pl. inocula): the form of a pathogen that is capable of causing infection.

lesion: a localized area of diseased tissue; a common disease symptom.

mesocotyl: the plant tissue that connects the seed and seminal roots to the crown of a developing corn seedling.

microsclerotium (pl. microsclerotia): tiny survival structures produced by some fungi (*see also* sclerotium).

monogenic: a type of resistance that is controlled by one gene.

mosaic: a pattern of light and dark areas on a leaf; often a symptom of a virus disease.

mottle: the scattering or irregular occurrence of light and dark areas on plant tissue; often a symptom of a virus disease.

mycelium (pl. mycelia): the threadlike vegetative form of a fungus.

mycotoxin: a chemical compound that is produced by certain fungi and is toxic to humans and livestock.

necrosis (adj. **necrotic**): the death of plant tissue.

nematode: a small, nonsegmented roundworm that causes plant disease.

oomycete: a classification of fungal-like organisms such as *Pythium* species; also called water molds.

oospore: the thick-walled survival spore of some oomycetes.

pathogen (adj. **pathogenic**): a disease-producing agent; often used to refer to an infectious agent, such as a virus, bacterium, fungus, or parasite.

perithecium (pl. **perithecia**): a fungal fruiting structure; shaped like a flask.

polygenic: a type of resistance that is controlled by many genes.

proliferation: the quick growth of new plant tissue.

pustule: a small, raised spot that breaks through the surface layer of plant tissue.

pycnidium (pl. **pycnidia**): a fruiting structure of some fungi in which conidia are formed; shaped like a flask.

rugosity: a condition of being rough and wrinkled.

saprophyte: an organism that survives by consuming dead organic matter.

sclerotium (pl. **sclerotia**): a hard mass of hyphae that can survive harsh conditions.

seminal roots: lateral roots that develop after the radicle (the first plant part to grow out of the planted seed) on a germinating corn seedling.

senescence (v. **senesce**): the decline and eventual death of plant tissue that occurs naturally because of aging.

sign: a physical indication of a pathogen—for example, a fungal fruiting body or bacterial ooze.

solanaceous: a classification of plants that includes potatoes, tomatoes, and many weeds; members of the nightshade family.

specialty corn: a category of corn that includes popcorn, sweet corn, seed corn, food-grade corn, and corn grown in organic production systems.

spore (v. **sporulate**): a microscopic particle that allows a fungus to reproduce; may adapt for dispersal and survival.

stoma (pl. **stomata**): a natural opening in a leaf that allows the exchange of air.

subsp.: abbreviation for "subspecies"; can be used following a scientific name to designate a type within the species that is genetically unique.

symptom: any detectable change in color, shape, and/or function of a plant in response to a pathogen or disease-causing agent.

tillage: preparation of the soil for growing a crop; can include breaking down crop residue and thus reducing levels of inoculum and insect pests.

topography: the physical or natural features of the land.

toxin: a poison.

vector: an organism that spreads a pathogen.

virulent: capable of causing severe disease.

water soaking (adj. **water-soaked**): the condition of being wet and translucent; pertains to a type of lesion often seen early in the development of a bacterial disease.

zoospore: a spore produced by an oomycete; able to swim in water.

IMAGE CREDITS

Cover Image

© Scott Sinklier/AgStock Images/Corbis.

Maps

Steve McKinley, York, Pennsylvania.

Interior Images

Part One

Courtesy Kiersten Wise—Used by permission.

Chapter 2

Fig. 2.1, Courtesy Kiersten Wise—Used by permission.

Fig. 2.2, Courtesy Gary Munkvold—Used by permission.

Fig. 2.3, Courtesy Craig Grau—Used by permission.

Fig. 2.4, Courtesy Alison Robertson—© APS.

Fig. 2.5, Courtesy Tom Hillyer—Used by permission.

Fig. 2.6, Courtesy Iowa State University Extension and Outreach—Used by permission. Graphic artist, Renée Tesdall.

Fig. 2.7, Courtesy Martha Patricia Romero Luna—Used by permission.

Fig. 2.8, Courtesy Daren Mueller—Used by permission.

Fig. 2.9, Courtesy Gary Munkvold—Used by permission.

Fig. 2.10, Courtesy Craig Grau—Used by permission.

Fig. 2.11, Courtesy Alison Robertson—© APS.

Fig. 2.12, Courtesy Nolan Anderson—Used by permission.

Fig. 2.13, Courtesy John Hill—Used by permission.

Fig. 2.14, Courtesy Iowa State University—Used by permission.

Fig. 2.15, Courtesy Iowa State University Extension and Outreach—Used by permission. Graphic artist, Renée Tesdall.

Fig. 2.16, Courtesy Kiersten Wise—Used by permission.

Fig. 2.17, Courtesy Adam Sisson—Used by permission.

Fig. 2.18, Courtesy Craig Grau—Used by permission.

Fig. 2.19, Courtesy Kiersten Wise—Used by permission.

Fig. 2.20, Courtesy Adam Sisson—Used by permission.

Fig. 2.21, part A, Courtesy Kiersten Wise—Used by permission; **part B,** Courtesy Adam Sisson—Used by permission.

Fig. 2.22, Courtesy Kiersten Wise—Used by permission.

Fig. 2.23, Courtesy Iowa State University Extension and Outreach—Used by permission. Graphic artist, Renée Tesdall.

Fig. 2.24, Courtesy Daren Mueller—Used by permission.

Fig. 2.25, Courtesy Kiersten Wise—Used by permission.

Fig. 2.26, Courtesy Kiersten Wise—Used by permission.

Fig. 2.27, Courtesy Adam Sisson—Used by permission.

Fig. 2.28, Courtesy Alison Robertson—© APS.

Fig. 2.29, Courtesy Mark Licht—Used by permission.

Part Two

Courtesy Brian Lang—Used by permission.

Chapter 3

Fig. 3.1, Courtesy Daren Mueller—Used by permission.

Fig. 3.2, Courtesy Kiersten Wise—Used by permission.

Fig. 3.3, Courtesy Kiersten Wise—Used by permission.

Fig. 3.4, Courtesy Kiersten Wise—Used by permission.

Fig. 3.5, Courtesy Heather M. Kelly—Used by permission.

Fig. 3.6, Courtesy Gary Munkvold—Used by permission.

Fig. 3.7, Courtesy Kiersten Wise—Used by permission.

Fig. 3.8, Courtesy Daren Mueller—Used by permission.

Fig. 3.9, Courtesy Gary Munkvold—Used by permission.

Fig. 3.10, Courtesy Craig Grau—Used by permission.

Fig. 3.11, Courtesy Alison Robertson—© APS.

Fig. 3.12, Courtesy Gary Munkvold—Used by permission.

Fig. 3.13, Courtesy Kiersten Wise—Used by permission.

Fig. 3.14, Courtesy Craig Grau—Used by permission.

Fig. 3.15, Courtesy Alison Robertson—© APS.

Fig. 3.16, Courtesy Emerson Nafziger—Used by permission.

Fig. 3.17, Courtesy Kiersten Wise—Used by permission.

Fig. 3.18, Courtesy J. K. Pataky—© APS. Reproduced, by permission, from G. P. Munkvold and D. G. White. 2016. Compendium of Corn Diseases, 4th ed. American Phytopathological Society, St. Paul, MN.

Fig. 3.19, Courtesy Kiersten Wise—Used by permission.

Chapter 4

Fig. 4.1, Courtesy Alison Robertson—© APS.

Fig. 4.2, Courtesy Kiersten Wise—Used by permission.

Fig. 4.3, Courtesy Alison Robertson—© APS.

Fig. 4.4, Courtesy Tom Allen—© APS.

Fig. 4.5, Courtesy William Dolezal and Pioneer Hi-Bred International, Inc.—Used by permission.

Fig. 4.6, Courtesy Kiersten Wise—Used by permission.

Fig. 4.7, Courtesy Alison Robertson—© APS.

Fig. 4.8, Courtesy Daren Mueller—Used by permission.

Fig. 4.9, Courtesy Gary Munkvold—Used by permission.

Fig. 4.10, Courtesy Daren Mueller—Used by permission.

Fig. 4.11, Courtesy Daren Mueller—Used by permission.

Fig. 4.12, Courtesy Greg Shaner—Used by permission.

Fig. 4.13, Courtesy Daren Mueller—Used by permission.

Fig. 4.14, Courtesy Greg Shaner—Used by permission.

Fig. 4.15, Courtesy William Dolezal and Pioneer Hi-Bred International, Inc.—Used by permission.

Fig. 4.16, Courtesy Roger Vinande and Pioneer Hi-Bred International, Inc.—Used by permission.

Fig. 4.17, part A, Courtesy Brigitte Duval—Used by permission; part B, Courtesy Alison Robertson—© APS.

Fig. 4.18, Courtesy Gary Munkvold—Used by permission.

Fig. 4.19, Courtesy Alison Robertson—© APS.

Fig. 4.20, Courtesy Daren Mueller—Used by permission.

Fig. 4.21, Courtesy Kiersten Wise—Used by permission.

Fig. 4.22, Courtesy Kiersten Wise—Used by permission.

Fig. 4.23, Courtesy Carl Bradley—Used by permission.

Fig. 4.24, Courtesy Carl Bradley—Used by permission.

Fig. 4.25, Courtesy Alison Robertson—© APS.

Fig. 4.26, Courtesy Craig Grau—Used by permission.

Fig. 4.27, Courtesy Daren Mueller—Used by permission.

Fig. 4.28, Courtesy Kiersten Wise—Used by permission.

Fig. 4.29, Courtesy Kiersten Wise—Used by permission.

Fig. 4.30, Courtesy Adam Sisson—Used by permission.

Fig. 4.31, Courtesy Kiersten Wise—Used by permission.

Fig. 4.32, Courtesy Adam Sisson—Used by permission.

Fig. 4.33, Courtesy Kiersten Wise—Used by permission.

Fig. 4.34, Courtesy Alison Robertson—© APS.

Fig. 4.35, Courtesy Alison Robertson—© APS.

Fig. 4.36, Courtesy Adam Sisson—Used by permission.

Fig. 4.37, Courtesy Gary Munkvold—Used by permission.

Fig. 4.38, Courtesy Greg Shaner—Used by permission.

Fig. 4.39, Courtesy Kiersten Wise—Used by permission.

Fig. 4.40, Courtesy Daren Mueller—Used by permission.

Fig. 4.41, Courtesy Kiersten Wise—Used by permission.

Fig. 4.42, Courtesy Daren Mueller—Used by permission.

Fig. 4.43, Courtesy Kiersten Wise—Used by permission.

Fig. 4.44, Courtesy Gail Ruhl—Used by permission.

Fig. 4.45, Courtesy Daren Mueller—Used by permission.

Fig. 4.46, Courtesy William Dolezal and Pioneer Hi-Bred International, Inc.—Used by permission.

Fig. 4.47, Courtesy Gary Payne, from Bugwood.org—Used by permission.

Fig. 4.48, Courtesy L. Stewart, C. Nacci, and K. Chamberlain. Reproduced from G. P. Munkvold and D. G. White. 2016. Compendium of Corn Diseases, 4th ed. American Phytopathological Society, St. Paul, MN.

Fig. 4.49, Courtesy Daren Mueller—Used by permission.

Fig. 4.50, Courtesy Daren Mueller—Used by permission.

Fig. 4.51, Courtesy Daren Mueller—Used by permission.

Fig. 4.52, Courtesy Daren Mueller—Used by permission.

Fig. 4.53, Courtesy Craig Grau—Used by permission.

Fig. 4.54, Courtesy Craig Grau—Used by permission.

Fig. 4.55, Courtesy Craig Grau—Used by permission.

Fig. 4.56, Courtesy Alison Robertson—© APS.

Fig. 4.57, Courtesy Kiersten Wise—Used by permission.

Fig. 4.58, Courtesy Kiersten Wise—Used by permission.

Fig. 4.59, Courtesy Alison Robertson—© APS.

Fig. 4.60, Courtesy Alison Robertson—© APS.

Fig. 4.61, Courtesy Alison Robertson—© APS.

Fig. 4.62, Courtesy Gail Ruhl—Used by permission.

Fig. 4.63, Courtesy Craig Grau—Used by permission.

Fig. 4.64, part A, Courtesy Greg Shaner—Used by permission; part B, Courtesy Craig Grau—Used by permission.

Fig. 4.65, Courtesy Daren Mueller—Used by permission.

Fig. 4.66, Courtesy Kiersten Wise—Used by permission.

Fig. 4.67, Courtesy Daren Mueller—Used by permission.

Fig. 4.68, Courtesy Daren Mueller—Used by permission.

Fig. 4.69, Courtesy Tom Isakeit—© APS.

Fig. 4.70, Courtesy Thomas Lugod and Pioneer Hi-Bred International, Inc.—Used by permission.

Fig. 4.71, Courtesy Tom Isakeit—© APS.

Fig. 4.72, Courtesy Tom Isakeit—© APS.

Fig. 4.73, Courtesy Daren Mueller—Used by permission.

Fig. 4.74, Courtesy Craig Grau—Used by permission.

Fig. 4.75, Courtesy Craig Grau—Used by permission.

Fig. 4.76, Courtesy Adam Sisson—Used by permission.

Fig. 4.77, Courtesy Alison Robertson—© APS.

Fig. 4.78, Courtesy John Obermeyer—Used by permission.

Fig. 4.79, Courtesy Alison Robertson—© APS.

Fig. 4.80, Courtesy Gary Munkvold—Used by permission.

Fig. 4.81, Courtesy Gary Munkvold—Used by permission.

Fig. 4.82, Courtesy Alison Robertson—© APS.

Fig. 4.83, Courtesy Alison Robertson—© APS.

Fig. 4.84, Courtesy J. K. Pataky—Used by permission.

Fig. 4.85, Courtesy Howard Schwartz and Great Plains Diagnostic Network—Used by permission.

Chapter 5

Fig. 5.1, Courtesy Greg Shaner—Used by permission.

Fig. 5.2, Courtesy Kiersten Wise—Used by permission.

Fig. 5.3, Courtesy Kiersten Wise—Used by permission.

Fig. 5.4, Courtesy Alison Robertson—© APS.

Fig. 5.5, Courtesy Alison Robertson—© APS.

Fig. 5.6, Courtesy Craig Grau—Used by permission.

Fig. 5.7, Courtesy D. G. White. Reproduced from G. P. Munkvold and D. G. White. 2016. Compendium of Corn Diseases, 4th ed. American Phytopathological Society, St. Paul, MN.

Fig. 5.8, Courtesy Carl Bradley—Used by permission.

Fig. 5.9, Courtesy Alison Robertson—© APS.

Fig. 5.10, Courtesy Marcelo Echagüe and Pioneer Hi-Bred International, Inc.—Used by permission.

Fig. 5.11, Courtesy Alison Robertson—© APS.

Fig. 5.12, Courtesy Tamra Jackson-Ziems—© APS.

Fig. 5.13, Courtesy Heather M. Kelly—Used by permission.

Fig. 5.14, Courtesy Tom Hillyer—Used by permission.

Fig. 5.15, Courtesy Tamra Jackson-Ziems—© APS.

Fig. 5.16, Courtesy Tom Hillyer—Used by permission.

Fig. 5.17, Courtesy Tamra Jackson-Ziems—© APS.

Fig. 5.18, Courtesy J. D. Mueller—© APS. Reproduced, by permission, from G. P. Munkvold and D. G. White. 2016. Compendium of Corn Diseases, 4th ed. American Phytopathological Society, St. Paul, MN.

Fig. 5.19, Courtesy Travis Faske—Used by permission.

Fig. 5.20, Courtesy Travis Faske—Used by permission.

Fig. 5.21, Courtesy Travis Faske—Used by permission.

Chapter 6

Fig. 6.1, Courtesy Alison Robertson—© APS.

Fig. 6.2, Courtesy Alison Robertson—©APS.

Fig. 6.3, Courtesy Alison Robertson—© APS.

Fig. 6.4, Courtesy Alison Robertson—© APS.

Fig. 6.5, Courtesy Daren Mueller—Used by permission.

Fig. 6.6, Courtesy Daren Mueller—Used by permission.

Fig. 6.7, Courtesy Daren Mueller—Used by permission.

Fig. 6.8, Courtesy Gary Munkvold—Used by permission.

Fig. 6.9, Courtesy Gary Munkvold—Used by permission.

Fig. 6.10, Courtesy Gary Munkvold—Used by permission.

Fig. 6.11, Courtesy Alison Robertson—© APS.

Fig. 6.12, Courtesy Gary Munkvold—Used by permission.

Fig. 6.13, Courtesy Gary Munkvold—Used by permission.

Fig. 6.14, Courtesy Alison Robertson—© APS.

Fig. 6.15, Courtesy D. G. White. Reproduced from G. P. Munkvold and D. G. White. 2016. Compendium of Corn Diseases, 4th ed. American Phytopathological Society, St. Paul, MN.

Fig. 6.16, Courtesy Gary Munkvold—Used by permission.

Fig. 6.17, Courtesy Alison Robertson—© APS.

Fig. 6.18, Courtesy Alison Robertson—© APS.

Chapter 7

Fig. 7.1, Courtesy Iowa State University Extension and Outreach—Used by permission. Graphic artist, Renée Tesdall.

Fig. 7.2, Courtesy Gary Munkvold—Used by permission.

Fig. 7.3, Courtesy Kiersten Wise—Used by permission.

Fig. 7.4, Courtesy Alison Robertson—© APS.

Fig. 7.5, Courtesy Alison Robertson—© APS.

Fig. 7.6, Courtesy Gary Munkvold—Used by permission. Reproduced from G. P. Munkvold and D. G. White. 2016. Compendium of Corn Diseases, 4th ed. American Phytopathological Society, St. Paul, MN.

Fig. 7.7, Courtesy Carl Bradley—Used by permission.

Fig. 7.8, Courtesy Alison Robertson—© APS.

Fig. 7.9, Courtesy Martha Patricia Romero Luna—Used by permission.

Fig. 7.10, Courtesy Adam Sisson—Used by permission.

Fig. 7.11, Courtesy Carl Bradley—Used by permission.

Fig. 7.12, Courtesy Gary Munkvold—Used by permission.

Fig. 7.13, left, Courtesy Alison Robertson—© APS; **right,** Courtesy Kiersten Wise—Used by permission.

Fig. 7.14, Courtesy Alison Robertson—© APS.

Fig. 7.15, left, Courtesy Gary Bergstrom—Used by permission; **right,** Courtesy Alison Robertson—© APS.

Fig. 7.16, Courtesy Gary Munkvold—Used by permission.

Fig. 7.17, Courtesy Charles Woloshuk—Used by permission.

Fig. 7.18, Courtesy Gary Munkvold—© APS. Reproduced, by permission, from G. P. Munkvold and D. G. White. 2016. Compendium of Corn Diseases, 4th ed. American Phytopathological Society, St. Paul, MN.

Fig. 7.19, Courtesy Gary Munkvold—Used by permission.

Fig. 7.20, Courtesy Gary Munkvold—Used by permission.

Fig. 7.21, Courtesy Gary Munkvold—Used by permission.

Fig. 7.22, Courtesy Charles Woloshuk—Used by permission.

Fig. 7.23, Courtesy Alison Robertson—© APS.

Fig. 7.24, Courtesy Gary Munkvold—Used by permission.

Fig. 7.25, Courtesy Gary Munkvold—Used by permission.

Fig. 7.26, Courtesy Gary Munkvold—Used by permission.

Chapter 8

Fig. 8.1, Courtesy Jim Camberato—© APS.

Fig. 8.2, Courtesy Kiersten Wise—Used by permission.

Fig. 8.3, Courtesy Gary Munkvold—Used by permission.

Fig. 8.4, Courtesy Brian Lang—Used by permission.

Fig. 8.5, Courtesy Josh Dunn—© APS.

Fig. 8.6, Courtesy Adam Sisson—Used by permission.

Fig. 8.7, Courtesy Kiersten Wise—Used by permission.

Fig. 8.8, Courtesy Adam Sisson—Used by permission.

Fig. 8.9, Courtesy Purdue University—Used by permission.

Fig. 8.10, Courtesy Mark Licht—Used by permission.

Fig. 8.11, Courtesy Dennis Bowman—Used by permission.

Fig. 8.12, part A, Courtesy Kiersten Wise—Used by permission; part B, Courtesy Daren Mueller—Used by permission; part C, Courtesy Craig Grau—Used by permission.

Fig. 8.13, Courtesy Kiersten Wise—Used by permission.

Fig. 8.14, Courtesy Daren Mueller—Used by permission.

Fig. 8.15, part A, Courtesy Kiersten Wise—Used by permission; part B, Courtesy Adam Sisson—Used by permission.

Fig. 8.16, Courtesy Kiersten Wise—Used by permission.

Fig. 8.17, Courtesy Kiersten Wise—Used by permission.

Fig. 8.18, Courtesy Adam Sisson—Used by permission.

Fig. 8.19, Courtesy Kiersten Wise—Used by permission.

Fig. 8.20, Courtesy Stephanie Porter, Burrus Sales Agronomist, and Austin Kocher, Burrus Intern—Used by permission.

Fig. 8.21, Courtesy Daren Mueller—Used by permission.

Fig. 8.22, Courtesy John Obermeyer—Used by permission.

Fig. 8.23, Courtesy John Obermeyer—Used by permission.

Fig. 8.24, Courtesy John Obermeyer—Used by permission.

Fig. 8.25, Courtesy John Obermeyer—Used by permission.

Fig. 8.26, Courtesy Gary Munkvold—Used by permission.

Fig. 8.27, Courtesy John Obermeyer—Used by permission.

Fig. 8.28, Courtesy John Obermeyer—Used by permission.

Fig. 8.29, Courtesy Alison Robertson—© APS.

Fig. 8.30, Courtesy Daren Mueller—Used by permission.

Chapter 9

Fig. 9.1, Courtesy J. K. Pataky—Used by permission.

Fig. 9.2, Courtesy Nyasha Chiuraise—Used by permission.

Fig. 9.3, Courtesy Samuel Gathama and Pioneer Hi-Bred International, Inc.—Used by permission.

Fig. 9.4, Courtesy J. K. Pataky—Used by permission.

Fig. 9.5, Courtesy J. K. Pataky—Used by permission.

Fig. 9.6, Courtesy Bob Kemerait, University of Georgia, from Bugwood.org—Used by permission.

Chapter 10

Fig. 10.1, part A, Courtesy Brandon Kleinke—Used by permission; part B, Courtesy Daren Mueller—Used by permission.

Fig. 10.2, part A, Courtesy Brandon Kleinke—Used by permission; part B, Courtesy Daren Mueller—Used by permission.

Fig. 10.3, Courtesy Alison Robertson—© APS.

Fig. 10.4, Courtesy Alison Robertson—© APS.

Fig. 10.5, Courtesy Craig Grau—Used by permission.

Fig. 10.6, Courtesy Gail Ruhl—Used by permission.

Fig. 10.7, Courtesy Craig Grau—Used by permission.

Fig. 10.8, Courtesy Nolan Anderson—Used by permission.

Fig. 10.9, parts A–C, Courtesy Brandon Kleinke—Used by permission; part D, Courtesy Nolan Anderson—Used by permission.

Fig. 10.10, Courtesy Brandon Kleinke—Used by permission.

Fig. 10.11, part A, Courtesy Daren Mueller—Used by permission; part B, Courtesy Adam Sisson—Used by permission.